**2021-22 EDITION**

# Prepare for Medicare

## THE INSIDER'S GUIDE TO BUYING MEDICARE INSURANCE

# Matt Feret

# Prepare
# for
# Medicare

## THE INSIDER'S GUIDE TO
## BUYING MEDICARE INSURANCE

### 2021-22 EDITION

# Matt Feret

Copyright 2021 © Matt Feret/MF Media, LLC

All rights reserved. No part of this book may be reproduced or transmitted in any form or by any means, electronic or mechanical, including photocopying, recording, or by any information storage and retrieval system without written permission of the publisher, except for the inclusion of brief quotations in a review.

Hardcover ISBN: 978-1-7372122-1-8

Paperback ISBN: 978-1-7372122-0-1

eBook ISBN: 978-1-7372122-2-5

## DISCLAIMER

This book is in no way associated, endorsed, or authorized by the Social Security Administration, the Department of Health and Human Services, or the Centers for Medicare and Medicaid Services. This book is in no way sponsored, associated, authorized, approved, endorsed nor, in any way affiliated with any company, trademarked names, or other marks. Any such mention is for purpose of reference only. Any advice, generalized statistics, or opinions expressed are strictly those of the author's, utilizing nearly two decades of Medicare insurance experience. Although every effort has been made to ensure the contents of this book are correct and complete, Medicare rules, premiums, and coverages change quickly and often. The book isn't meant to replace the sage advice of healthcare, insurance, financial planning, accounting, or legal professionals. You are responsible for your financial decisions. It is your sole responsibility to independently evaluate the accuracy, correctness or completeness of the content, services, and products of, and associated with this publication.

The thoughts and opinions expressed in this publication are those of the author only, and are not the thoughts and opinions of any current or former employer of the author. Nor is this publication made by, on behalf of, or endorsed or approved by any current or former employer of the author.

# TABLE OF CONTENTS

# SPECIAL INVITATION

Please note Medicare rules, regulations, policies and benefits change often. If you'd like to get the most up-to-date information, my insights, join a discussion or download free helpful checklists referenced in the book, come join us at PrepareforMedicare.com.

# INTRODUCTION

At some point, you and every other American close to or on Medicare will want the same thing—help! Help knowing when and how to sign up for Medicare. Help avoiding lifelong Medicare enrollment penalties. Help understanding Medicare insurance coverage options. Help deciding which Medicare insurance plan is "best." Help shopping for and buying Medicare insurance policies. Help finding a Medicare insurance agent or how to DIY. Help reviewing Medicare insurance coverage annually.

If you buy the "wrong" type of Medicare insurance and then decide it's not the best path for you, you may not be able to buy the "right" choice later on. Just because you made a choice at age sixty-five, doesn't mean it's still the right plan when you turn seventy.

Once you do make a choice, you're generally locked into that choice for an entire year.

Making the wrong Medicare insurance choice can cost you thousands of dollars, even tens of thousands of dollars.

Think about that. If each of us gets Medicare at age sixty-five and lives to age seventy-five, even a $1,000 mistake turns into a $10,000 mistake over ten years.

This book will guide you toward the right choices at the right time and in the right way for your individual needs, wants, and situation.

Following the steps I outline in this book will save you time, frustration, and money.

I know you're overwhelmed with advertising. You're overwhelmed with choices. Enrollment is a pain and it's unclear. Many of you reading this aren't sixty-five, but you're trying to help a loved one or client with their Medicare insurance.

This book will give you an insider's view of how to narrow the choices down and get the Medicare insurance policy that meets your needs, those of your loved ones or clients, without having to become a Medicare expert.

## THERE ARE USUALLY TWO TYPES OF MEDICARE CONSUMERS:

1.  I like to shop for the best deal. I like to research and know everything about a subject. I'm skeptical of salespeople, and I like to DIY everything. *(This starts in Chapter Nine.)*

2.  I don't like this whole process. I don't want to deal with it. Make it easy for me; do it for me or tell me how I can outsource this decision by using a Medicare insurance agent. *(This starts in Chapter 8.)*

This book is for both of you.

I want to be very clear here. *There are no "hacks" to Medicare.* There are no shortcuts; there are only longcuts. It's not simple, but I can make it simpler. Any book, video, website, blog, or pundit who says otherwise isn't being 100% truthful.

I can and will show you how to decide upon the best of three plan coverage options, how to choose a Medicare insurance policy and confidently DIY, or how to identify and use a professional Medicare insurance agent to check your work and research and enroll in a plan that suits your needs. Finally, I'll show you what you have to do every year to make sure your choice(s) are still good ones and what to do if you need to switch.

If you read and follow the directions in this book, shopping for your Medicare insurance plan for the first time when you're first eligible – whether that's right at age sixty-five or if you work past age sixty-five, should take somewhere in the neighborhood of two to four hours, max.

That's it.

If you read and follow the directions in this book, you should be re-shopping your Medicare insurance options every October to make sure you've still got the best plan that fits your needs. This should take one to two hours each October.

That's it.

## YOU HAVE OPTIONS – TOO MANY OPTIONS!

The good news—there are *only three ways* to "consume" your Medicare!

(I've **bolded** what you'll have to actually buy or purchase from a Medicare insurance company.)

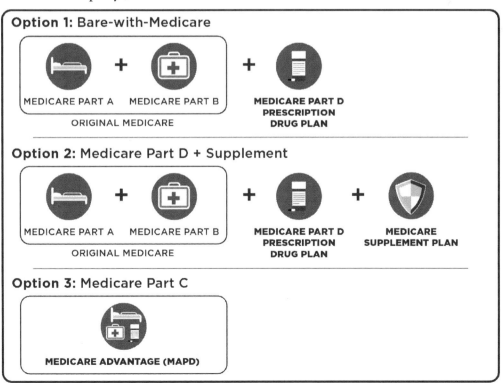

The bad news: *You have too many choices!*

Many of you reading this have only had a handful of choices every year to choose from when selecting insurance coverage from your employer. When you work for a company that offers health insurance benefits, you'd normally be offered two or three plans to choose from, each from the same insurance company. You might have spent ten or fifteen minutes deciding whether or not you wanted a PPO or an HMO the following year, or whether you wanted a $2,000 or a $4,000 deductible. Other than that, the choices you had to make were limited because you had few to pick from. The choices were few, the differences small, and it was all pretty easy and straightforward.

When you buy Medicare insurance, you have hundreds and perhaps thousands of Medicare insurance coverage choices to choose from.

Choosing which of the three paths is right for you can be confusing. Once you choose a path, it gets even more complicated because the number and combination of Medicare insurance policies you can buy in either option can be absolutely dizzying.

For instance, choosing the Medicare Advantage path, depending on where you live, could lead you to have to choose from more than fifty options, each with its own nuances. Each plan has different benefits, limitations on what doctors you can see, what prescription drugs are covered, and their prices. To top it off, most plans change prices, benefits, prescription drug formularies, and doctor coverage every single year.

These choices can be overwhelming for most people. Don't worry—it's not just you. Everyone is overwhelmed when faced with too many choices. This is what's known as "choice overload," and scientists have studied the phenomenon for a long time. Essentially, the research shows that people *think* they want a lot of choices. But, in reality, they get overwhelmed and confused when presented with too many. According to the research, when people are offered only six choices rather than twenty-four or thirty, they're less confused, get less frustrated, and are more satisfied with the choice they make. (Go to PrepareforMedicare.com/sources for all cited sources and to learn more.)

Choosing between the three plan coverage paths, then choosing from among those fifty or so Medicare insurance plan options, gets even more muddied because every company, every website, every "resource," and every insurance agent in your community seems to be trying to sell you something. Why? *Because they are.* There are healthy commissions to be made by selling you a Medicare insurance product.

That doesn't make Medicare insurance agents and company representatives bad people; far from it. In my experience, more than 70% of all Medicare insurance policies are sold through an agent. But finding that awesome agent who can give you wonderful guidance and has the experience, expertise, and perspective to assist in finding the best plan for *you* can be very tough.

The investment or mutual fund industry has what's known as "fee-only" advisors. They don't make a commission by selling you a stock or a mutual fund; you just pay them a fee or very small percentage of assets for managing your accounts. This arrangement is supposed to eliminate any chance that commissions will influence their mutual fund or stock recommendations.

Fee-only advisors don't really exist in the Medicare insurance space. Everyone in the Medicare insurance sales field makes a commission from selling you a Medicare insurance product unless you buy a policy directly from an insurance company's website or one of their employees on the phone.

I've been asked for years to help my friends and family (hi, mom!) to guide them through the Medicare insurance maze, which of course I do for free. I provide advice and perspective and help walk those friends and family members through the maze.

Obviously, I can't do this for everyone, so at some point, I'll probably have a Q&A section on my website, PrepareforMedicare.com, that addresses common questions. If you'd like, you can sign up for my newsletter there. Right now, you can also submit general questions anytime at questions@prepareformedicare.com. Please note: you won't want to give me detailed health or confidential information in your email; just ask basic questions. I'll choose the ones that occur most often and feature them in future blog posts or the newsletter.

Back to my point. Commissions are involved when buying Medicare insurance policies. Does the fact that Medicare sales agents make commissions when they sell you a Medicare insurance policy make it a flawed or subjective process? Because it's not a fee-only relationship, is that a bad thing? Is that wrong? My opinion is no, it's not bad or wrong, but you need to understand what you're getting into. I hold a very special place in my heart for independent Medicare insurance agents. The advice, perspective, and products they sell can be invaluable and a very important part of your financial and healthcare planning as you age. I'm a big fan.

However, your Medicare insurance agent may not be showing you the best plans for you because they're not able to, or they simply aren't comfortable selling that plan for some reason. You might be getting bad advice from friends and family or from websites and advertising. You might be in the wrong plan for your lifestyle and healthcare needs. You might be paying too high a percentage of your income for your health insurance. You might be paying too much premium money by not re-shopping every fall. You might not be getting the best deal for the premium money you're paying.

You're the only truly objective person out there.

Where on earth can you get honest, objective Medicare guidance without sitting through a sales pitch at the end? How can you do this without having to become a Medicare expert yourself? Don't you wish you were a close friend or family member of a Medicare insurance executive? Don't you wish you had someone on the "inside" to show you the way?

Well, now you do! I'm your guy, and this book is your guide.

## WHO AM I AND WHY DID I WRITE THIS BOOK?

First things first. I wrote this book to help you. I believe part of my purpose for being on this earth is to help, educate, and enrich the lives of my fellow human beings. If I can do that, I feel fulfilled.

I have more than twenty years of experience in the Medicare insurance field, and while I have my health insurance license, I'm not an independent insurance agent, nor have I ever been. Instead, I've worked on the inside of health insurance companies for decades.

Although most insurance agents you'll ever talk to have a financial interest in you purchasing an insurance policy, I have no driving motive other than ensuring you're informed, equipped, and confident in your choices. I want to be your trusted resource for accurate, real-time, valuable information that will save you time and money. I have no mission other than to simplify the Medicare insurance process for you.

The stats: I have bachelor's and master's degrees. I have held a health insurance license since 2002 and continue to take the same training and testing that agents are required by the government to pass every year to be able to sell Medicare insurance products.

I began my insurance career at the very lowest rung as a hard-working customer service rep and climbed my way up the corporate ladder to where I am today as an executive at a major health and wellness company. Along the way, I've answered thousands of phone calls from insurance policyholders, trained and certified thousands of independent insurance agents (maybe even yours!) and insurance call-center representatives, made hundreds of Medicare insurance industry presentations, and even lobbied Congress. I've developed Medicare insurance products that hundreds of thousands of people are enrolled in today (maybe even you!), led sales teams, marketing teams, call center teams, personally written hundreds of pages of policy and procedures, and worked on federal Medicare audits, compliance, and actuarial teams. I've worked in just about every facet of the Medicare health insurance field imaginable. In fact, I've worked for quite a few health insurance companies, large and small, so I know a lot of "inside baseball," top to bottom.

This experience has given me a unique perspective—one that very few people have. I straddle the lines—the public Medicare consumer on one side and the corporate and governmental Medicare ecosystem on the other. I keep up with all things Medicare every day. I keep up with it because I have to stay current with the legislation, policy and regulatory changes, and overall industry trends as part of my job. I also find it really interesting.

The result of this unique perspective is the book you're reading. My goal is to cut through all of the noise and hype to objectively help decipher and clarify what it all means to *you*.

Although I work for an insurance company, I'm not pushing any company over another – just so long as the plan you buy meets your healthcare and financial needs and goals. Again, no ulterior motive here—I'm not here to hype one way over the other, one insurance company over another. I'm here to help you navigate the maze, adding in some perspective and advice.

The thoughts and opinions expressed in this publication are those of the author only, and are not the thoughts and opinions of any current or former employer of the author. Nor is this publication made by, on behalf of, or endorsed or approved by any current or former employer of the author.

Throughout the book, I cite many outside sources. Head over to my website PrepareforMedicare.com/sources to view the links to them. I've also included a glossary of common Medicare terms and acronyms at the end of this book. For additional information or more in-depth discussion, you can find that on the website as well. It's important that you use *only* those links I provide at PrepareforMedicare.com/links and not click out of them, or you'll end up down the very same rabbit hole you've no doubt already found yourself in, wandering all over the internet, randomly reading blog posts.

## WHY IS THERE SO MUCH INFORMATION AVAILABLE?

The majority of the websites, blogs, and books out there just amount to different ways of trying to sell you something by re-packaging information from the Medicare website. Most of them do a decent job outlining government regulations and important dates. But, to me, they read like encyclopedias. There's no real original thought or advice to be found—no practical application, just rules and dates regurgitated on the screen or page. You can find those anywhere and everywhere, and it can all be very confusing. What you can't find anywhere is what I consider to be the most important information, such as:

- There are three viable options as a consumer to "consume" Medicare. What are they?

- How do you find a fantastic Medicare insurance agent or insurance technology company who will help you (or do it for you) along the way?

- What's better, Medicare Advantage or Medicare Supplement insurance? How do you decide? How do you know you're getting the "best" deal?

(Hint: I'm going to tell you!)

Just before your sixty-fifth birthday (and for the rest of your life), insurance companies will absolutely flood you with ads. Direct mail will jam your mailbox, TV and newspaper ads with smiling celebrities or unassuming presenters will urge you to call for "information," and blinking, flashing, pay-per-click advertising online will promise you the moon. Yet, for the more than sixty-seven million people already on Medicare and the estimated 11,000 "Baby Boomers" turning sixty-five every day, you must make your own coverage choices or else they'll be made for you, and you can be penalized for not taking action.

It almost goes without saying that we're an extremely diverse country with very different educational, financial, health, and lifestyle backgrounds. Every person nearing Medicare eligibility, or who is already on it, has a different way of thinking about where they are in life and about the future. Some might profess to be in perfect health but forget they're on cholesterol and blood pressure medicines that keep them that way. Some have been diabetic for thirty years and are concerned with how to keep it under control. Others have been healthy their whole lives and see no reason at all to worry about participating in programs that help them manage non-existent conditions. Some are happy with their financial outlook, while others worry about the future.

From Hollywood A-list celebrities to your unassuming neighbor, all of us have, or will eventually get, Medicare, regardless of income, where we live, our race, creed, religion, political leanings, etc. There's one commonality among all of us over the age of sixty-five—we have to choose how we will, or will not, insure ourselves for medical and prescription drug benefits while on Medicare.

Attitudes toward Medicare are all over the map. Some love the challenge—they dive into the specifics of Medicare, learn all they can, and make informed decisions about their coverage. Others absolutely dread shopping for insurance and would rather have an expert do it for them.

Plus, as I've already mentioned, there are thousands of options to choose from, and what might be the best choice for you may not be the best choice for Tom Cruise or your unassuming neighbor. In fact, what might be the best choice for you may not even be the best choice for your spouse or partner! There are not that many reasons why you and your spouse or partner have to have the exact same kind of coverage or even the same insurance company. Odds are, you don't see the same doctors or have the same medical conditions; why then would you have the same Medicare insurance policy? The Medicare insurance options on the market today can all be highly personalized and tailored to the individual.

I call sticking with Original Medicare Parts A and B for your healthcare coverage going "Bare-with-Medicare," which is what I'll call it going forward. (Catchy, isn't it?)

Do you go "Bare-with-Medicare," meaning, you stay on "Original Medicare" and just buy a Medicare Part D Prescription Drug Plan for drug coverage and call it a day? Do you buy a Medicare Supplement plan? How about this thing called Medicare Advantage?

Doing nothing isn't an option. You have to be proactive and make a choice or a series of choices. Doing absolutely nothing means you'll be assigned Original Medicare benefits anyway, and you'll get a penalty for not choosing a Medicare Part D Prescription Drug Plan when you should have. Or, if you're in a certain low-income bracket, Medicare will just automatically assign you a plan. Is that the way you want to get insurance coverage? Didn't think so.

# WHY MAKING THE RIGHT CHOICE IS SO IMPORTANT: THE STORIES OF TIM AND ALEX

Why is choosing the right Medicare insurance plan so important? Easy. One wrong move could cost you thousands of dollars. One wrong move could make you ineligible for coverage down the road. One wrong move could bar access to a prescription drug you need, a doctor you wish to see, or a hospital you want to use. One wrong move could make you miss out on valuable benefits you're eligible for . . . or not, if you have the right insurance coverage.

Let's look at an example:

> Tim and Alex both live in Miami, Florida. Both Tim and Alex, unfortunately, had heart attacks on New Year's Day at the exact same time and took an ambulance to the exact same hospital. They each spent five days in the hospital before being discharged. Both have Medicare Advantage plans but from different Medicare insurance companies.
>
> Tim pays $0 per month for his Medicare Advantage plan, as does Alex. Tim's Medicare Advantage plan uses an HMO (Health Maintenance Organization) network, while Alex's uses a PPO (Preferred Provider Organization) network.

## TIM: TREATED LIKE ROYALTY

When Tim got home, he ran across a note from someone from the insurance company trying to deliver a hot meal to him. That's when he realized he would get meals delivered to his door every day for the next ten days, free of charge, so he wouldn't have to cook. He also had a call waiting for him on his cellphone from a care coordinator who walked him through his follow-up appointments, prescription drugs, and at-home care.

Doctors were able to keep tabs on Tim through a remote-monitored EKG and interacted with him often by telephone and the occasional videoconference call right on his laptop. When Tim needed to attend doctor's appointments in person for checkups, the insurance company sent a car to his house, where he was picked up and dropped off at the doctor's office. Once his appointment was over, he was again picked up from the doctor's office and dropped off at his house. Tim's doctors also prescribed acupuncture to alleviate any additional pain Tim had because of his heart attack, which was also covered by his insurance. The insurance company even sent someone over to Tim's house to assess his mobility to see if there were any items they could install in his home that would help with accident prevention. One of Tim's new doctors helping him recover wasn't in the insurance company's network, but that was okay because all Tim had to do was ask his insurance company to find a doctor in the HMO network, which they did.

When all of Tim's medical and prescription bills finally came due, his total share of the cost for his heart attack came to $400. His Medicare insurance company charged him $0 for days one through five in the hospital, $25 per specialist visit to his cardiologists, and $100 for some diagnostic tests. The rest of the charges were from various copays for prescriptions he had filled at his local pharmacy.

## ALEX: AN EXPENSIVE EXPERIENCE LARGELY ALONE

When Alex got home, he arrived at an empty house and a list of prescriptions he should fill. No care coordinator or nurse ever called him to see how he was doing. His heart wasn't monitored in real-time. He was just told to get to the cardiologist's office four days after discharge for a follow-up appointment. When it came time to go to his appointment, he wasn't comfortable driving and had to call a few friends to see if they could take him. They couldn't, so he called an Uber and paid $30 for the round trip. Alex didn't have a telemedicine option; every follow-up doctor's visit had to be in-person. Alex was still in a lot of pain, and while his doctor also suggested that acupuncture could alleviate the pain, it wasn't covered under his insurance plan, so he had to pay cash. No one from the insurance company was sent to his house to see if he needed grip bars installed in his bathtub. One of Alex's new doctors wasn't in the insurance company's network. He was able to go anyway but was charged 50% of the cost of the visit, far more than the $25 it would have been had the doctor been in the network.

When all of Alex's medical and prescription bills finally came due, the total cost of his heart attack came to $6,000. His Medicare insurance company charged him $695 per day in the hospital but also a $1,300 deductible on top of that. He had to pay a separate $325 deductible for his prescription drugs before his benefits kicked in as well. He had to pay for transportation to his doctor's appointments and acupuncture out of his own pocket. His visit to the cardiologist out-of-network cost him another $250. His son came over to install grip bars in his bathroom, so he, fortunately, didn't have to pay for that!

## WAIT, WHAT?

Wait a second—how could Alex's bill be *more than ten times* higher than Tim's for the exact same heart attack, at the same time at the same hospital? Well, that's because Tim clearly chose a Medicare Advantage plan that offered far more financial protection and additional health-related services than Alex did, even though they lived in the same city.

This example is based on a true story. While Tim and Alex are fake people, the Medicare Advantage plans I used as examples for each are 100% real and available *right now.* Fake Tim and Alex have forty-three(!) different Medicare Advantage options available for purchase in Miami. As you can see, picking the wrong one could literally be a decision that will not only cost you thousands of dollars but, more importantly, could cost you your health. It's not just a Miami thing—I could tell similar stories using examples found in every state in the Union. The myriad of choices available makes it tough to find the right one for *you,* but it's not impossible.

Even if you've already made Medicare insurance choices, this isn't a one-time decision. Just as your financial situation, health, and living arrangements change, so do the benefits and premiums of Medicare insurance policies. The insurance choices you have, the enrollment periods, and the options and information are always changing and changes every year. That's why you need to review your coverage *every year.*

Sticking your head in the sand won't help; standing idly by while the calendar turns into a new year could cost you thousands of dollars. How do you know if you're in a quality, reputable plan? Paying too much? Using a high-quality, reputable, expert Medicare insurance agent? If you're a caregiver helping your parents or other family members decide, what's your role? Where can you turn for objective guidance?

## MAKE THE SYSTEM WORK FOR YOU!

Don't feel bad. Don't feel overwhelmed, sad or exasperated. From GED to Ph.D., this is confusing and frustrating for everyone, including my mom (who has an Ed.D). She calls me every September, annoyed and confused at all of the mail she gets from her current insurance carrier, other insurance carriers, and changes being made to her policy. She says, "Matt, can you just review this for me and tell me which one I should pick?" Of course, I do because she's my mom. But not everyone has a family member who has worked for Medicare insurance companies for twenty years.

It doesn't need to be this hard. It doesn't need to be this frustrating. It's really not as hard as you think, and it's not as confusing as it seems.

Along our journey together, I'm going to teach you only what you need to know and how to filter out all the noise (and there's a *lot* of noise). I will teach you how to pick out the plan that's best for you, and save you hours and days that you could and should be spending doing something you enjoy.

This book will show you how to do four things:

**1** How to sign up and when to sign up for Medicare and how to avoid late-enrollment penalties.

**2** How to choose one of the three insurance coverage paths to confidently find the right Medicare insurance plan(s) for *you.*

**3** How to confidently do it yourself (DIY) or identify a professional Medicare insurance agent to help you navigate through the maze.

**4** What you need to review every single October, no matter how old you are or what plan you have. Every. Single. Year.

## A FINAL NOTE FOR SPECIAL SITUATIONS

This book is for "most people." In other words, the vast majority of you fit into what I've laid out in the pages that follow.

"But Matt, what happens if I'm living in a chateau in France when I turn sixty-five? What do I do then?" Well, there's an answer for that, but I'm not going to address it. Nor will I address similar one-off or unique situations that only apply to a small number of people—not in this book anyway. But there are additional items on my website PrepareforMedicare.com you might find useful. Quite frankly, if you have a special situation like that, you should skip right to Chapter Eight in this book and find out how to talk to a Medicare insurance agent or a company representative and let the Medicare professionals and experts help you. Using a book or doing Google searches for hours will only waste time.

I'll obviously cover the most common what-if scenarios, but not an exhaustive list of scenarios. I didn't want to write an encyclopedia because no one (yours truly included) wants to read an encyclopedia. You don't need to be an expert in Medicare to buy Medicare insurance. You need a baseline—a general understanding of Medicare—and that's what I've written for you. My goal is to educate you with a base amount of useful information, help you decide what Medicare insurance coverage might be right for you, and then light the path to buying your Medicare insurance without distraction and sales pitches so you can move on with your life. In the end, your insurance coverage decisions are yours alone.

# KEEP THESE POINTS IN MIND, AND LET'S GET STARTED!

Before we begin, let me share a few thoughts to keep in mind:

- The authors of the books I've read are either currently independent insurance agents making commissions by selling Medicare insurance, financial planners making commissions via financial planning, self-described "experts" like me (there's no certification for that), or reporters. I've seen low-priced or "free" books being used as essentially marketing pieces to draw people into a conversation that the authors hope will eventually lead to a sale and a commission. Some are reporters, probably none of whom have ever spent a day working for an insurance company. This doesn't make them wrong or bad people; it just means I have a different perspective.

- Most authors, bloggers, websites, and "helplines" advertised on TV and direct mail pieces are trying to do one thing—generate sales leads and sales to make a commission. Either that or they're using it as branding to *eventually* have a shot at selling you some type of insurance or financial product. Again, I am not doing this.

- Some books are sponsored by insurance companies or "non-profit" entities that receive millions of dollars of fees from insurance companies. My book is not sponsored by anyone.

- Many blogs and websites offer a snippet of correct information but don't give it all away because they want you to call them so they can start the sales process. Don't fall for that.

- Medicare insurance companies and agencies market to you not based on what you *should* buy, but what they *want* you to buy. Medicare insurance companies and agencies market to you based on what they *think* they know about you and how likely it is you'll buy what they're selling. Medicare insurance companies and agencies market to you (or do not) after doing extensive research as to how competitive they think their product is in the marketplace that particular year, *not* based on what type of product is the best fit for *you* or where *you* live. *You* are the only person who knows your specific healthcare needs, your financial risk tolerance levels, your specific budget, and your personal preferences when it comes to "consuming" your Medicare benefits.

So, stop staring at that pile of direct mail on your countertop, throw all the insurance company brochures away, quit watching the pseudo-celebrity TV commercials, and stop clicking on random websites. This book boils it down to what really matters: quickly understanding Medicare basics, narrowing your choices, finding and buying the best Medicare insurance plan for your specific needs, buying one within your budget, and quickly reviewing your coverage every October.

Throughout the book, I'll be highlighting a few tips and observations you should pay special attention to, or things I think are specifically important. I've called each a *Matt Tip*. Matt Tips will be noted by icons like this:

Now, let's begin with some Medicare insurance basics.

# CHAPTER ONE

# WHAT IS MEDICARE?

Original Medicare is medical insurance for people over the age of sixty-five, and people under sixty-five with a long-term disability, or those who have certain disabilities like End-Stage Renal Disease (ESRD) or Amyotrophic Lateral Sclerosis (ALS), commonly known as Lou Gehrig's disease. Once you're eligible, there's no need to medically "qualify" for Medicare—you get it regardless of your current health. There are no health questions you need to answer to get Medicare. Once you have it, you cannot get kicked off of it for any medical condition or health-related reason. While there are certain limitations to care, and monthly premiums may differ from individual to individual, it does not "run out."

There are four parts of Medicare. Medicare Part A and Medicare Part B were the original choices rolled out in the 1960s. Thus, Original Medicare refers to Medicare Part A and Part B; Part C and Part D were added later. It's a bit of an alphabet soup, but I'll briefly explain what each letter does (and doesn't) mean below.

 **MEDICARE PART A:** hospital insurance covers inpatient hospital care, skilled nursing facility, hospice, surgery, and some home health care.

**MEDICARE PART B:** helps pay for services from doctors and other health care providers, outpatient care, lab tests, some home health care, and durable medical equipment.

 **MEDICARE PART C:** also known as Medicare Advantage. These are typically "combo" products of Medicare A, B, and D, although some *do not* include Part D (more on that later in the book). These are only sold by insurance companies.

 **MEDICARE PART D:** helps pays for "retail" prescriptions, usually at your local pharmacy or via mail-order. Part D is used in two ways:

1. Embedded into certain Medicare Advantage plans (MAPD plans).

2. Offered as a stand-alone prescription drug insurance policy, used in conjunction with Original Medicare A and B medical coverage and oftentimes alongside a Medicare Supplement plan. Also commonly referred to as a Medicare Part D Prescription Drug plan, or a PDP.

Part D does not cover medical procedures—it only covers prescription drugs. These are only sold by insurance companies.

 **MEDICARE SUPPLEMENTS:** also referred to as "Medigap" plans, Medicare Supplements are insurance policies that help cover the deductibles, coinsurance and copays Original Medicare A and B doesn't pay for. These are also only sold by insurance companies.

Medicare was established on July 30, 1965, by President Lyndon Johnson, and—fun fact—the first Medicare recipients were President Harry Truman and his wife, Bess.

When the George W. Bush administration oversaw the passage of the 2003 Medicare Modernization Act, they made two hugely positive changes to Medicare that influence what you can buy, what it costs, and what it covers to this very day.

First of all, the Medicare Modernization Act introduced prescription drug coverage, also called Medicare Part D. From 1965 until the act was implemented in the 2005–2006 timeframe, people on Medicare had to pay full price for prescription drugs at the pharmacy out of their own pockets. Yes, it covered drugs needed in a hospital setting for, say, anesthesiology to put you under for surgery, and covered some other drugs under Medicare Part B. But if you had a statin for your cholesterol that you filled at the pharmacy, prior to the passage of the new Act, you paid for that 100% out of your pocket.

The second thing this Act did was increase payments and provided incentives for insurance companies to offer things called "Medicare Advantage plans," also known as Medicare Part C. If you're on Medicare and are reading this, you've probably heard all about these, and one-third of you have one for your Medicare insurance coverage. These plans were also introduced to the masses in the 2005–2006 timeframe, and the insurance companies who jumped at the chance to offer these products earlier than others were Humana and UnitedHealthcare, as well as some other smaller or start-up companies who have since been largely swallowed up by bigger insurance companies.

Until the Medicare Modernization Act was passed and insurance companies began rolling out Medicare Part D Prescription Drug Plans and Medicare Advantage plans to the masses, you basically had two choices to make when you turned sixty-five. One choice was "free" in that, besides having a small monthly premium for Medicare Part B deducted from your Social Security check, you just "got" Medicare Parts A and B. The only other choice was to buy "extra" insurance. That "extra" insurance was a Medicare Supplement plan. You simply paid for prescription drugs out of your pocket.

Fast forward to today; the Medicare insurance field has become vastly more complex for you, the Medicare consumer. Quite frankly, it's become vastly more complex for Medicare insurance companies and Medicare insurance agents, too. Decades ago, you only had one choice to make when you turned sixty-five—whether or not to buy a Medicare Supplement Plan. Today, you essentially have three:

**1** stay on Original Medicare and only buy a Medicare Part D Prescription Drug Plan or,

**2** stay on Original Medicare and buy a Medicare Part D Prescription Drug Plan and a Medicare Supplement Plan or,

**3** buy a Medicare Advantage plan that includes Medicare Part D benefits

Today, any of those three options lead you down a dizzying array of rabbit holes with potentially hundreds of additional choices. As a consumer, you now have thousands of combinations and choices on your Medicare menu.

Do we really need all of these choices? Is choice a good thing? Isn't there something to be said for simplicity? In my experience, people don't necessarily want more choice; what they want is to feel more confident in the choices they *do* make. When you're done reading this book, I guarantee you'll at least be more *confident* in the choices you make—either on your own or with the help of a Medicare insurance agent.

*Throughout the book, I refer to Medicare as "Original Medicare." This means Medicare Part A and Medicare Part B.*

# THE A, B, C'S (AND D) OF MEDICARE

Let's dive into some specifics around each letter.

## MEDICARE PART A

This is hospital coverage, hospice, and skilled nursing care. For most people, this doesn't cost you anything; it's an entitlement program because you and your company have essentially already paid your portion through payroll taxes while you or your spouse were working. You get it at no cost if you or your spouse have been working for at least ten years and you've been a permanent, legal resident of the US for five continuous years. If none of the above applies (which is rare), you can buy Part A, and it will cost between $259 and $471 per month (in 2021), depending on how long you worked or your particular circumstance.

## MEDICARE PART B

This covers doctors' visits, services provided by doctors while in the hospital, ambulance rides, outpatient procedures, durable medical equipment (things like oxygen machines, CPAP devices, blood sugar monitors, diabetic test strips, etc.), and a very small number of prescription drugs (which are often extremely expensive). These include drugs typically administered by a doctor, particularly those drugs used in the treatment of cancer, chemotherapy, immunosuppressants, or infusion therapy. You must pay a monthly premium for Part B, normally right out of your Social Security check. In 2021, it's $148.50 per month for most people.

Part B also covers home health services (but not custodial care), preventive screenings and counseling, outpatient physicals, occupational and speech therapy, mental health, x-rays, and lab tests. It basically covers (almost) everything Part A does not, with the exception of retail prescription drugs, which are covered under Part D.

## MEDICARE PART C

This is also called Medicare Advantage. Medicare Advantage plans are only sold by authorized insurance companies. You cannot buy a "federal" or a "public option" Medicare Advantage plan. Medicare Advantage comes in a few shapes and sizes, but the vast majority of them are technically called "Medicare Advantage-Prescription Drug" plans. You might see or hear about this as the acronym MAPD, pronounced by spelling it out, M-A-P-D. These are essentially combo plans. They combine the medical coverage of Original Medicare Parts A and B *and* prescription drug benefits under Medicare Part D into one plan, Medicare Part C.

There are also Medicare Advantage plans that do *not* come with Medicare Part D Prescription Drug benefits. These are known as MA-only plans. This is pronounced by spelling it out, too. M-A-only. These plans are specifically designed for the approximately nine million Veterans who have pharmacy benefits through the Veterans Administration (VA) and TRICARE. I'll address these later.

Additionally, there are Medicare Advantage plans called Special Needs Plans. You might see or hear these referred to by the acronym SNP, pronounced "snips." Dual-SNPs are sometimes available for people on Medicare and Medicaid (a state-government program that helps pay health care costs for people with resources) although, they're not made as available as regular Medicare Advantage plans. As of 2020, about 2.8 million Americans are enrolled in Dual-SNPs. There are also SNP plans for people in nursing homes or other facilities, or who have chronic or disabling health conditions such as congestive heart failure. These are often referred to as C-SNPs or Institutional SNPs, and they're pretty rare. Under one million people are on these (Source: PrepareforMedicare.com/sources).

The premiums for these plans normally range from $0 to around $100 per month, although they can be higher.

## MEDICARE PART D

This is the stand-alone prescription drug plan you add to your Medicare coverage if you don't have a Medicare Advantage plan with Medicare Part D Prescription Drug benefits already embedded (MAPD) or get it through your employer's retiree plan. I address employer plans in Chapter Eleven. These are also called Part D plans, referred to by the acronym PDP, or Medicare Part D Prescription Drug Plans.

*Throughout the book, when I'm referring to stand-alone Part D plans you add to Original Medicare or Medicare Supplement coverage, I'll use the phrase: Medicare Part D Prescription Drug Plans.* Monthly premiums for this range from around $8 to around $60 per month, depending on where you live.

## HOW MUCH DOES MEDICARE COST? MEDICARE MONTHLY PREMIUMS

Previously, I summarized "normal" premiums for Medicare Parts A ($0), Part B ($148.50, 2021), Part C ($0-100+), and Part D ($8-$60). Again, that's for most people. There are exceptions to these; if you make (or have) a lot of money, you pay more. And if you do not have a lot of money, you pay less or nothing at all.

Medicare Part B isn't fully funded by payroll taxes like Part A is because Medicare rules say around 25% of all Part B expenses must come from people on Medicare. That's why you're charged a premium for Part B. It's not important to remember the exact amount because you need it and will just have to pay for it. Besides, it's not that much money if you compare it to what you were paying for your employer-sponsored or Affordable Care Act coverage when you were working. Just know it's there and it'll go up almost every year, and it normally comes out of your Social Security check automatically.

Part B isn't an entitlement, but you will get it automatically with Part A if you are drawing Social Security. Otherwise, you'll need to apply for it. If you work past age sixty-five and have employer health insurance, you can also opt out of it until you stop working and retire. Part B comes with a monthly premium. Again, in 2021 that monthly premium is $148.50 per month for most people. I say most people, but that premium can be different because it increases every year, and it's also means-tested. Means-testing is a fancy way of saying it depends on how "rich" you are. If you make more, you're going to pay more. Much more.

The official name is Income-Related Monthly Adjustment Amount or IRMAA, and it's pronounced like someone's name, "Irma." Boy, oh boy, people do not like IRMAA. She pops up later in Medicare Part D, too.

Medicare looks back at your tax returns from two years ago to determine how much you made. If you made less than $87,000 per year filing single, or $174,000 per year filing jointly, you can skip the next paragraph. They use something called Modified Adjusted Gross Income (MAGI), which is your Adjusted Gross Income with some of your deductions added back in.

If you make a lot of money, you will pay a higher premium for Part B. If you make over $500,000 per year, you could pay $504.90 (2021) per month!

You can figure out your Medicare Part B premium costs by going to the website PrepareforMedicare.com/links and looking for Part B costs in the links section. They change every year, and the table is updated annually.

Most people pay the standard Part B premium amount. If your modified adjusted gross income as reported on your IRS tax return from two years ago is above a certain amount, you'll pay the standard premium amount and an IRMAA on top.

Your Medicare Part B premium is typically automatically deducted from your Social Security, Railroad Retirement Board, or Office of Personnel Management benefits. If you don't have enough money to pay this out of any of those, then Medicare will bill you directly for the unpaid balance. If you're not drawing Social Security, you'll be billed quarterly.

If you disagree with the way the Social Security Administration has processed your tax information or simply think it's wrong, *file an appeal.* **You can save hundreds of dollars a year if they favorably redetermine your income.** In other words, if you think you're being charged too much, you can appeal it. As you can imagine, in true bureaucratic fashion, there's a form to fill out. You can request an appeal in writing by completing a Request for Reconsideration (Form SSA-561-U2), or you may contact your local Social Security office to file your appeal. You can find the appeal form online at https://www.ssa.gov/forms/ssa-561.pdf. Alternatively, head over to PrepareforMedicare.com/links for the form.

## MEDICARE PREMIUM ASSISTANCE

If you need it, there are ways to potentially pay less for not only your Medicare Part B premiums, but also Part D premiums. There are several programs, some from the states and some from the federal government and they're all awarded based on income thresholds.

The various state and federal programs get a little confusing, but a good rule of thumb is if you make more than approximately $18,000 per year as an individual or approximately $28,000 as a couple, you won't qualify for any of these programs.

There are also differences in what you'll potentially pay for Medicare Part D depending upon your income. If the government decides you need, or you apply for and get accepted to receive what's called Extra Help, you won't pay full price for Medicare Part D. If you make more than approximately $20,000 per year as an individual or $26,000 as a couple, you probably won't qualify and will have to pay full price. There are asset considerations, too, such as home ownership, mutual funds, etc., so if this applies to you, keep reading.

There are four levels of Extra Help. The first level means you'll automatically be assigned a Medicare Part D plan because you have both Medicare and Medicaid, you're in a Medicare Savings Program, or you get Supplemental Security Income (SSI) benefits. If you already have a Medicare Part D Prescription Drug Plan or have Part D prescription drugs through your Medicare Part C (MAPD plan), you can keep it and might get a premium discount. There are three other levels, and they're all income- and assets-based.

If you're on Medicaid or collect Supplemental Security Income from Social Security, you shouldn't have to apply for Extra Help.

You can apply for Extra Help at Social Security, and the form can be found on the website PrepareforMedicare.com/links. You can also call Social Security at 1-800-772-1213.

Medicare publishes a handy chart that outlines all the help available in detail, and you can find it on the website, too. You'll find it here: PrepareforMedicare.com/links.

## OTHER WAYS TO GET ORIGINAL MEDICARE

Didn't work and are divorced? Recently immigrated to the United States? Unsure if you qualify for Medicare? There are other ways to get Original Medicare.

- If you're married for at least a year and your spouse is eligible for Social Security benefits when you turn sixty-five.

- If you are divorced but were married for ten or more years, you're covered if your former spouse is eligible for Social Security.

- If you're a widow or widower (and currently single) and were married for nine or more months to someone who was eligible for Social Security.

- If you are considered disabled for at least twenty-four months or are eligible for receiving retirement benefits from Social Security or the Railroad Retirement Board.

- You can also get Part A if you are a kidney dialysis patient or have received a kidney transplant.

If you want to check your eligibility, you can go to the website at PrepareforMedicare.com/links.

Before we go any further, here's a list of what *isn't* covered under Original Medicare Part A and B:

1. Retail prescription drugs (covered under Part D, which we will get to soon)

**2** Custodial care (help with bathing, dressing, using the bathroom, and eating)

**3** Long-term care (nursing homes, retirement homes, and assisted living facilities)

**4** Cosmetic surgery

**5** Most chiropractic services when not medically necessary

**6** Routine dental and vision services

**7** Most care while traveling outside the United States (we'll get to this, too)

There are all sorts of other health-related items Original Medicare A and B do not cover, which insurance companies can provide in certain circumstances. In 2019 and 2020, the Trump administration gave Medicare insurance companies even more flexibility to offer additional benefits to improve in-home care setups and services. It also made changes to allow Medicare insurance companies to allow greater telemedicine and remote-access healthcare for its customers. Medicare insurance companies are allowed to include these types of benefits in their Medicare Advantage plans. However, this type of flexibility is not yet being introduced in Original Medicare Parts A and B. This feeds into one of the "Frustrating Flaws" of Medicare, which are coverage limitations. I'll cover these in Chapter Three.

The additional items Medicare insurance companies can include in their insurance coverage are:

✓ Private hospital room or private nursing in the hospital

✓ Healthy food dollar amount allowances at grocery stores

✓ Adult daycare visits and personal home helpers

- ✓ Lifestyle drugs, including erectile dysfunction prescriptions
- ✓ Air conditioner allowances for people with COPD and asthma
- ✓ Transportation to doctor's appointments
- ✓ Nutritional programs, personal trainers, and access to spas
- ✓ Grocery delivery
- ✓ Flexible dollar amount allowances for healthcare-related items at select retailers (sometimes in the hundreds of dollars per year)
- ✓ Acupuncture and massage therapy
- ✓ Gym memberships or fitness classes
- ✓ Weight management programs
- ✓ Dental insurance and dentures
- ✓ Routine eye exams and glasses
- ✓ Routine hearing tests and hearing aids
- ✓ In-home safety assessments and services

# USING ORIGINAL MEDICARE BENEFITS: COSTS

Now that you understand what Original Medicare is, a general idea of what it does and doesn't cover, how you can sign up if you need to, and how much it costs, let's get to how much using your Original Medicare benefits will cost you.

### MEDICARE PART A

There are Part A deductibles you must pay before your insurance benefits kick in. However, it's not an annual deductible (payable once a year); it's a "Benefit Period" deductible. What's the difference? Glad you asked.

According to Medicare, a benefit period begins the day you're admitted as an inpatient in a hospital or Skilled Nursing Facility. The benefit period ends when you haven't gotten any inpatient hospital care (or skilled care in a Skilled Nursing Facility) for sixty days in a row. If you go into a hospital or a Skilled Nursing Facility after one benefit period has ended, a new benefit period begins. You must pay the inpatient hospital deductible for each benefit period. In 2021, the deductible is $1,484 per benefit period, and this amount normally increases every year. However, there's no limit to the number of benefit periods during any given year.

Got that? It's not an annual deductible, so you actually could pay that deductible more than once during a calendar year.

After you've paid your benefit period deductible, after a certain number of days in a hospital or Skilled Nursing Facility, you'll also have to pay a copay every day. Don't worry about memorizing these numbers; just know they're there and they change, but not drastically.

**Inpatient Hospital Coverage:**

- If you're hospitalized, you'll first pay your $1,484. That covers your hospitalization bills up to sixty days.

- If you stay between 61-100 days, divide the deductible by four— you'll be charged another $371 per day. (I agree with you, that's quite a bit of money!)

- If you stay beyond 100 days, divide the deductible by two—days 101 to 150 will cost you $742 per day.

- Anything over 150 days, you'll be on the hook for 100% of the charges. Yikes.

- If you're hospitalized for psychiatric care, the benefits are slightly different. You have a 190-day lifetime benefit and some coverage changes. Go to PrepareforMedicare.com/links for links to more information.

As mentioned above, Part A also covers Skilled Nursing Facility care. **This is *not* Long-Term Care Insurance. Medicare does not cover Long-Term Care Insurance.** It also does not include "custodial care," which is care provided for things called "Activities of Daily Living." These are essentially things you need to do to care for yourself, such as eating, bathing, and moving around.

As such, Skilled Nursing Facility care isn't meant to be a long-term solution for patients. Think of it as an in-between step sometimes taken from the hospital to home, or from the hospital to a Long-Term Care facility.

### Skilled Nursing Facility Coverage:

- If you're in for under twenty-one days, you'll pay $0.

- Days 21-100, you'll pay up to $185.50 coinsurance per day (in 2021).

- Days 100+ you're on the hook for 100%.

What are the odds you will stay in a Skilled Nursing Facility for over 100 days? Very low. But even if you stay in for say, forty days, the quick math there is nineteen days X $185.50 = $3,524.50. That's in addition to anything you might owe from your prior hospitalization. Oh, one more thing. To get into a Skilled Nursing Facility, you'll first have to be an inpatient at a hospital for three days. Yep, this means you'll pay that deductible for the hospital stay in addition to the cost of the Skilled Nursing Facility care, so add the $1,484 on top of that number. This catches many people Bare-with-Medicare or who are on a Medicare Supplement plan by surprise. **If there's not a prior three-day stay in a hospital, Medicare won't approve a Skilled Nursing Facility stay, which can financially expose you to *the entire* Skilled Nursing Facility bill.**

Truthfully, a $1,484 deductible for a hospital stay is a pretty decent insurance benefit. Those of you coming off of an employer-sponsored plan probably had deductibles well above that when you were working. As we'll cover later, this is less out of your pocket for an inpatient hospital visit than many Medicare Advantage plans will charge you. It's the sixty-one or more days that should rightfully scare you.

Quick Math: if you stay hospitalized for 100 days, you'll owe the $1,484 deductible plus 39 X $371 = $15,953. Yikes! If you stay 150 days, it will total $57,134. Yikes again!

What are the odds you'll be in the hospital for more than 100 days and still be alive? Probably pretty low. Still, in my opinion, this highlights one of the major "Frustrating Flaws" of Original Medicare, and it comes up time and time again. There is no "stop-loss" or "Maximum Out Of Pocket (MOOP)." I'll get to this concept in a bit. Just stick with me here.

## MEDICARE PART B

Like Medicare Part A, there is an annual deductible you must pay before Medicare Part B benefits kick in. For 2021, the deductible is $203. *Unlike* Part A, there's only one deductible (no "Benefit Periods" apply here), and after you pay that deductible, you're on the hook for 20% of the remaining costs. Medicare pays the other 80%. Sounds simple, right?

Well, of course, it's not that simple. There's a catch to that 20% too. Medicare will pay 80% of the *allowed* charges. In some cases (somewhat rare, but it happens), a doctor or some other type of provider is allowed to charge up to 15% more than the Medicare *allowed* charge. There's a reason this happens, but it's not important. The important thing is, this is allowed to happen, and if it does happen, you're on the hook for the extra 15%. These are called Medicare Excess Charges.

If you have an outpatient procedure that falls under Medicare Part B, you're on the hook for 20% of it. This doesn't sound too bad for a $1,000 chemotherapy treatment, but when was the last time you heard of a chemotherapy treatment that only costs $1,000? Me either.

Quick Math: Let's say the surgery costs $20,000 and that's the Medicare-allowable amount. That means you're on the hook for 20% of that, or $4,000, after your deductible (which, remember, is $203 if you haven't already paid it for the year).

More Quick Math: Using the same scenario above, if this particular doctor charges the Medicare Excess Charge, that charge would be $23,000. Medicare would *approve* the $20,000, then you'd pay your 20% of that ($4,000) and then 100% of the extra "excess" of $3,000. So, in this example, your bill would be $7,000, plus (potentially) your annual Part B deductible.

Wow. Really? Yes. In my opinion, this is another one of the *Four Frustrating Flaws* of Original Medicare. There are Medicare insurance options available that *fix* this by introducing annual out-of-pocket spending maximums – a MOOP. This is another reason people buy other Medicare insurance on top of, or in place of, Original Medicare.

What else? Yep, you guessed it. There's no MOOP to Medicare Part B, either.

## MEDICARE PART D PRESCRIPTION DRUG PLAN

For those of you who are sticklers for alphabetical consistency, you'll notice I went from Medicare Part A, to Part B, skipped over Part C, and went right to D. There's a reason for this, which will become clear later on, so just stick with me.

Medicare Part D covers most prescription drugs. What I'm referring to in this section is a stand-alone *Medicare Part D Prescription Drug Plan*. This is different from a Medicare Advantage plan, which is technically Medicare Part C, and a "combo" product which you can read about in the next section. I agree, it gets confusing, though, because the vast majority of Medicare Advantage plans have Part D embedded into it (MAPD).

Unlike Parts A and B, you don't get this automatically (unless your annual income is below about $15,000 for individuals and $30,000 for couples), and you can't sign up for this the same way you did for Part A or Part B. Nor can you sign up for it through Social Security. That's because Medicare Part D Prescription Drug Plans are only sold by insurance companies. These insurance companies are essentially sub-contractors for Medicare. When you buy one, the premium and benefits are generally good for an entire calendar year.

If you want to buy a Medicare Part D Prescription Drug Plan, you must also have Original Medicare Part A *or* B. A lot of authors, reporters, and bloggers get this one wrong. You don't have to have *both* A and B—just one of them. Of course, if you have both, you're fine too.

When you go to buy a Medicare Part D Prescription Drug Plan (explained later in Chapters Eight and Nine), you'll be faced with a ton of options. By my last count, every state has at least twenty-five Medicare Part D Prescription Drug Plan options to choose from. Don't worry—I have the "prescription" to make it super easy for you to narrow down your choices and buy one. As long as you can click through a few steps on the Medicare.gov website, it's actually a bit of a breeze. We'll cover that in the DIY chapter. Or you can use a Medicare insurance agent. We'll cover both in a chapter later in the book.

You'd sign up for a stand-alone Medicare Part D Prescription Drug Plan if you (a) went Bare-with-Medicare and stuck with Original Medicare Parts A and B for your medical coverage or (b) stuck with Original Medicare Parts A and B for your medical coverage and bought a Medicare Supplement to fill in the gaps.

You'll hear people refer to this as a Medicare Part D Prescription Drug Plan, a PDP, or a Medicare Part D drug plan—all sorts of things. Think of this as the prescription drug card you show at the pharmacy counter or use when those same pharmacies mail you prescriptions. Some prescription drugs are covered under Medicare Part B, but those are generally administered in the hospital or an outpatient facility, like chemotherapy or dialysis drugs. Some drugs are covered under Part A but usually only when you're in a Skilled Nursing Facility, or during a hospital stay. Either way, your month-to-month retail prescription drugs (high blood pressure, cholesterol, etc.) are covered under Medicare Part D.

Recent studies show that about 19% of the Medicare population buy a stand-alone Medicare Part D Prescription Drug Plan alongside Original Medicare—between 30-40% of people combine this with a Medicare supplement plan. Monthly premiums can vary from as low as $8 to as high as over $100, depending on the company, the number of drugs covered, and the plan design (Sources: PrepareforMedicare.com/sources). Most people pick a plan between $8 and $30 per month.

Medicare sets a "standard" or "minimum" Medicare Part D Prescription Drug Plan design for insurance companies to offer. Many offer plans that cover the gaps outlined below, usually for a higher premium.

There are four benefit phases of every "standard" Medicare Part D Prescription Drug Plan, and they reset every year on January 1. This isn't something you can pick or change; it's what the federal government decided was the way these would work. However, Medicare insurance companies can offer better benefits than just the standard plans, and many do. For example, there are many plans for sale that eliminate the deductible in Phase 1 but still follow this four-phase approach.

A byproduct of this four-phase approach is that, very likely, you won't pay the same amount for the same prescription at the pharmacy for the entire year. It'll be a moving target as you wander through these stages, so don't be surprised. There's nothing for you to track; the Medicare insurance company tracks all of this for you. You may be able to use mail-order to get lower prices, and of course, check other in-network pharmacies.

**PHASE 1**—This is the deductible phase. In 2022, you pay 100% of your prescription costs until you are at $480 out-of-pocket. This amount goes up every year, sometimes a little, sometimes a lot. Again, there is good news—there are a number of Medicare insurance companies that offer plans with zero deductible.

**PHASE 2**—This is called the Initial Coverage period. In 2022, after Phase 1, you pay a copay for each prescription until the total drug costs (what you and the Medicare insurance company spend, including any deductible) reach $4,430. This also typically goes up every year.

**PHASE 3**—This is called the Coverage Gap or "doughnut hole" and kicks in when the total prescription spending is between $4,430 - $7,050 (2022). This stage has really improved for consumers over the last few years. The insurance company doesn't pay any benefits at this stage, but you get discounts from drug manufacturers and the government during this stage. You exit the coverage gap when your total out-of-pocket cost on covered drugs (not including premiums) reaches $7,050 for the year. Your out-of-pocket cost is calculated by adding together all of the following: yearly deductible, coinsurance, and copayments from the entire plan year, and what you paid for drugs in the coverage gap (including the discounted amounts you didn't pay in that stage). At the risk of repeating myself, there's nothing for you to do or track here.

**PHASE 4**—This is called the Catastrophic Coverage phase. Once your out-of-pocket cost totals $10,690.20 (2022) in a given year, you exit the gap and get catastrophic coverage. In the catastrophic stage, you will pay a low coinsurance or copayment amount (which is set by Medicare) for all of your covered prescription drugs. That means the plan and the government pay for the rest—about 95% of the cost. You will remain in this phase until January 1 of the next year.

Sound confusing? It kind of is–until you get used to it. There are a few things to remember:

- Each Medicare insurance company selling Medicare Part D Prescription Drug Plans must offer a*t least* the minimum plan design described above. A large number of them also sell enhanced plans that eliminate the deductible and provide additional coverage through stages 2-4. This is primarily because they compete against other Medicare insurance companies for your business; they want you to buy their product.

- Each Medicare insurance company tracks the four phases as you go through them for you. There's nothing for you to do or track.

- Benefits reboot every January 1 for all Medicare Part D Prescription Drug Plans. (They also reboot January 1 for Prescription Drug Plans embedded into a Medicare Advantage plan, too.)

- There is no 4th quarter "carry-over" feature like some employer-based health insurance plans have. So, if you were used to getting "credit" in the following year for paying deductibles or co-insurance in the 4th quarter in the prior year, Medicare doesn't do that. Hypothetically, you could pay your deductible on December 31 and then pay it again on January 1.

✔ Each insurance company has its own formulary, which is a list of drugs they cover on their plan. No two companies have the exact same one, but Medicare makes them cover at least two drugs in each "class" of medications that treat a condition. They might not be the drugs you take, but *some* companies might cover yours. Yes, they change the drugs covered in the formularies and also change how much they cost every year. That's why it's important to make certain you check every October to see if you're still in the best plan for you, something I cover in Chapter Ten.

✔ Each insurance company has its network of preferred, or "in-network," pharmacies you can go to. Many have "preferred" and "non-preferred" lists, and you'll get the best bang for your buck at the "preferred" pharmacies. Why? Essentially, insurance companies contract better pricing (for them and often, for you) with those preferred pharmacies and do not get the same deals with non-preferred pharmacies.

✔ Many insurance companies offer mail-order prescription delivery, and it's often cheaper than filling them at your local pharmacy.

✔ If you can use the internet, there's a relatively painless way to go about buying a Medicare Part D Prescription Drug Plan all by yourself. In my opinion, it's the easiest Medicare insurance benefit to buy without the assistance of an insurance agent. Just type in your drugs, look up the pharmacy you go to, and Medicare.gov spits out what plan is probably best for you. I'll cover this step-by-step in Chapter Nine.

As you can imagine, this coverage doesn't come cheaply for taxpayers. The premium you pay only covers 17% of the program's cost. Financing for Medicare Part D comes from general tax revenues (71%), beneficiary premiums (17%), and state contributions (12%) (Sources: PrepareforMedicare.com/sources).

The top five Medicare Prescription Drug Companies by the number of customers they have are outlined below, courtesy of the Kaiser Family Foundation (the latest information they have at this writing is from 2019).

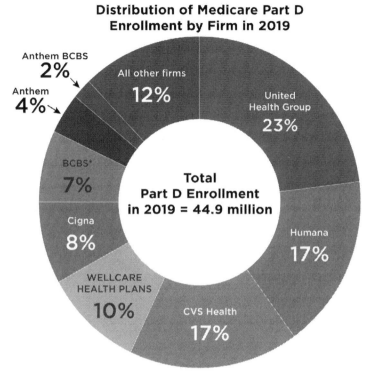

**Distribution of Medicare Part D Enrollment by Firm in 2019**

Total Part D Enrollment in 2019 = 44.9 million

- Anthem BCBS 2%
- Anthem 4%
- All other firms 12%
- United Health Group 23%
- BCBS* 7%
- Cigna 8%
- WELLCARE HEALTH PLANS 10%
- CVS Health 17%
- Humana 17%

NOTE: Includes enrollment in the territories and employer-only group plans.
*BCBS excludes Anthem BCBS, which is a separate plan sponsor.

## PART D AND IRMAA

Remember when we covered Medicare Part B, I told you how the more money you make or the richer you are, the more you're going to pay for your Part B? It's the same situation with Medicare Part D. The Income-Related Monthly Adjustment Amount (IRMAA) applies. Yes, IRMAA rears her ugly head here, too.

If you make $88,000 (2021) or less a year filing individual tax returns, you don't have to deal with IRMAA. The same goes if you're filing jointly and under $176,000 (2021) per year. Above those amounts, you're going to pay more for your Medicare Part D benefits, regardless of what the Medicare insurance company's premiums say they are on their marketing or plan documents. The amounts can be as little as an additional $12.30 per month, all the way up to an additional $77.10 per month.

These charts are published at different times of the year. Head over to the website PrepareforMedicare.com/links for an up-to-date chart.

If you're subject to this, Part D IRMAA payments are required, whether you receive your Medicare Part D coverage through a stand-alone Medicare Part D Prescription Drug Plan or through a Medicare Advantage plan that includes prescription drug coverage (MAPD).

**People affected by the 2021 IRMAA will get a letter from the Social Security Administration notifying them of their IRMAA payment.**

If you believe you have been wrongly charged IRMAA or have had a change in income, you can appeal your IRMAA or ask for a reassessment. You can request an appeal in writing by completing a Request for Reconsideration (Form SSA-561-U2), or you may contact your local Social Security office to file your appeal. You can find the appeal form online at http://www.socialsecurity.gov/online or request a copy through their toll-free number at 1-800-772-1213 (TTY 1-800-325-0778).

Alternatively, you can head to the website PrepareforMedicare.com/links and find all the links and forms there.

## PRESCRIPTION DRUG DISCOUNT PROGRAMS

One final note on prescription drug discount programs before we move on to the next section.

There are a number of companies out there spending enormous amounts of advertising money touting their programs as a way to save people money at the pharmacy counter. You may have heard of them: GoodRx, WeRx, Blink Health, and Optum Perks are just a few examples.

This is great! Anything that enables people to spend less on prescriptions is a good thing. Unfortunately, you cannot use a discount program and Medicare insurance *at the same time*. The discount programs don't work with Medicare Part D Prescription Drug Plans, or Part D plans embedded within a Medicare Advantage plan (MAPD). Technically, they will work at the pharmacy counter (meaning, you can use the discount card and still receive a discount on your prescription) but using this card instead of your Medicare Part D benefits—either through a Medicare Part D Prescription Drug Plan or a Medicare Advantage plan—means the prescription costs won't count towards the four phases outlined previously. **If you use a discount card, the Medicare Part D insurance company can't track your prescription drug costs and spending through the four phases because they don't know you're purchasing prescriptions using a discount card.**

**Essentially, if you're using a discount program and not your Part D Medicare benefits, what you're doing is paying cash (with the discount) for that prescription, and the Medicare insurance company doesn't know you're filling a prescription.** This is potentially problematic because if the Medicare insurance company can't track your prescription drug spending, whatever you buy with a discount card won't apply to your deductibles and coinsurance. Once you do use your Part D benefits, none of the prescriptions bought with the discount card or program will have applied to your Medicare Part D coverage.

Thus, I'd recommend not using a discount card to pay for your medications if you're on Medicare, unless your Medicare insurance company accepts it and manually adjusts your account. But that's up to the insurance company and, from the looks of it, isn't a set-in-stone option.

Here's what GoodRx says about this on their website: *Paying with a GoodRx coupon is considered an "out-of-network" purchase, and it's up to the insurance company to decide if they'll pay you back—or whether they'll count it toward your deductible* (Sources: PrepareforMedicare.com/sources).

## MEDICARE PART C—MEDICARE ADVANTAGE

Part C is also known as Medicare Advantage. Sometimes it's referred to as a Medicare Advantage Prescription Drug plan—an acronym you'll see and hear a lot—MAPD, pronounced M-A-P-D.

What follows is again, a brief overview because I cover Medicare Advantage in-depth a little later in the book.

Medicare Advantage plans can be thought of as "combo" plans. They combine the benefits of Medicare Part A, Part B, and Part D into one health insurance plan. (This is why I covered Part D first!)

To sign up for a Medicare Advantage plan, you *must* also have Medicare Part A and Part B, and you'll have to continue paying that Part B premium even if you're on a Medicare Advantage plan. You can't drop Part B and stay on a Medicare Advantage plan.

There is no medical underwriting required. You can be a marathon runner or a current cancer patient—it doesn't matter. The Medicare insurance companies have to accept you if you want to enroll in a Medicare Advantage plan.

If you sign up for a Medicare Advantage plan, you won't need to buy a stand-alone Part D Prescription Drug Plan in most cases. In fact, you can't have a Medicare Part D Prescription Drug Plan and a Medicare Advantage plan (MAPD) at the same time because, in the vast majority of circumstances, these plans come with Part D embedded within them.

In other words, Part D is included in almost every Medicare Advantage plan out there. There are exceptions to this called Medicare Advantage-Only plans (MA-only), and they usually only make sense for veterans (and even then, only sometimes). There are also other plan types available on a very limited basis: PFFS Medicare Advantage plans, Cost Plans, and Medicare Medical Savings Account plans (MSA). Cost Plans and PFFS plans are relics and largely unavailable; MSA plans are extremely niche products that, so far, have not gained a lot of traction with those on Medicare. I address Veterans and MA-only plans in Chapter Eleven.

Also, **you cannot have a Medicare Supplement and a Medicare Advantage Plan at the same time.**

Medicare, the governmental agency, doesn't sell Medicare Advantage plans. Just like Medicare Part D, insurance companies act as sub-contractors for Medicare. These insurance companies basically take a fee or an allowance from the federal Medicare program and take over the responsibility of paying claims from Medicare.

Insurance companies that offer Medicare Advantage plans do so on the condition that they are offering an insurance policy that is equal to or better than Original Medicare Parts A, B, and D. *They aren't allowed to offer a Medicare*

*Advantage plan that's worse than the benefits offered by Original Medicare.* These insurance companies also have the flexibility to include things Original Medicare does not cover.

For instance, many insurance companies add in additional benefits, such as vision, hearing, and dental coverage to sweeten the pot. Some even include transportation to doctors' appointments, acupuncture, adult daycare, meals, and gym memberships. In other words, many insurance companies cover additional health-related items Original Medicare doesn't.

Medicare allows insurance companies to offer these products on an annual basis, from January 1 to December 31 every year. For that year, they must keep their benefits and premiums the same. However, insurance companies add or delete benefits, and raise and lower premiums, quite literally every single year. One year, your prescription drugs might be covered at one copay level—the next year, they're not. Your primary care physician's copay may change. Your hospitalization benefits may get worse. They may get better! In fact, the insurance companies can decide to just cancel the entire plan (it happens more often than you think) at year-end, leaving you scrambling to find other coverage. Either way, the companies must let you know all of the upcoming changes by October 1 of every year. This is why, if you're considering purchasing or already have a Medicare Advantage plan, you *must* review your coverage every October.

In 2020, more than one-third (36%) of all Medicare beneficiaries—24.1 million people out of sixty-seven million Medicare beneficiaries overall—were enrolled in Medicare Advantage plans; this rate has steadily increased over time since the mid 2000s. Between 2019 and 2020, total Medicare Advantage enrollment grew by about 2.1 million beneficiaries or 9%—nearly the same growth rate as the prior year. The Congressional Budget Office (CBO) projects that the share of all Medicare beneficiaries enrolled in Medicare Advantage plans will rise to about 51% by 2030. (Sources: PrepareforMedicare.com/sources).

The top five Medicare Advantage Companies by the number of customers they have are outlined below, courtesy of the Kaiser Family Foundation (the latest information they have at this writing is from 2019).

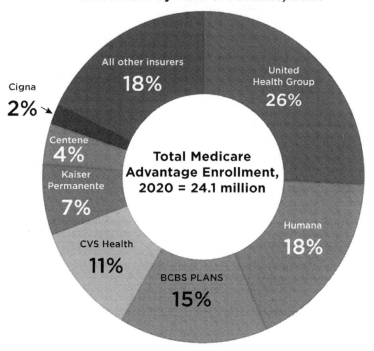

**Medicare Advantage
Enrollment by Firm or Affiliate, 2020**

Total Medicare Advantage Enrollment, 2020 = 24.1 million

- All other insurers 18%
- United Health Group 26%
- Cigna 2%
- Centene 4%
- Kaiser Permanente 7%
- CVS Health 11%
- BCBS PLANS 15%
- Humana 18%

NOTE: All other insurers includes firms with less than 2% of the total enrollment.
BCBS are BlueCross and BlueShield affiliates and includes Anthem BCBS.
Anthem non-BCBS plans are less then 2% of total enrollment.
Percentages may not sum to 100% due to rounding.

Sources: Prepareformedicare.com/sources

# CHAPTER TWO

# ENROLLMENT AND ELECTION PERIODS, LATE ENROLLMENT PENALTIES, AND MEDICARE STAR RATINGS

If you've done any research on the internet, talked to friends about Medicare, or leafed through the government-issued *Medicare and You* book, no doubt you've probably already heard about enrollment penalties. You'll have financial penalties that will follow you for the rest of your life if you don't sign up for Medicare Part B and Medicare Part D on time. That much is true. However, in this section, I'll explain how they work and how to avoid them.

To get there, we first need to talk about Election Periods. Election Periods outline *when* you can enroll in Medicare and Medicare insurance plans and outline special circumstances for just about every scenario out there.

Each of the Election Periods has an acronym associated with it for just about every scenario out there. Enrollment and election are often used interchangeably, which can be confusing. Making matters worse, there are a *ton* of these acronyms, more than thirty by my count.

Recently released from jail? Welcome back! There's a code for that. The

Medicare Advantage plan you have is pulling out of your service area? There's a code for that. Couldn't enroll in the insurance plan of your choice due to a FEMA-declared, weather-related emergency or disaster? Yep, there's a code for that.

Don't worry, you don't need to know all of them, or even most of them, really, and you don't need to remember the acronyms. You just need to know they're there, and that you can use them.

**Insurance company telephone reps all know these rules, as do good independent Medicare insurance agents. It's their job to know. So, if you've got a good agent, ask him or her to walk you through this if you need to, but not when you've got a week until your 65th birthday. You technically can do it then, but I would advise you to plan it out well in advance, if possible. Nothing ever goes 100% to plan when it's rushed. Do it sometime in the year leading up to your birthday or when you're eligible for Medicare so you can plan it out, especially if you have a special scenario. Common scenarios are (a) I'm still working past sixty-five, (b) my spouse or partner is younger than me and on my employer-sponsored group health insurance, (c) I'm disabled but have not yet surpassed my twenty-four months of Social Security Disability to qualify for Medicare, but it's coming up, or I spend part of the year overseas, am moving, etc.**

The four Election Periods I think you should be aware of are found on the pages that follow. That doesn't mean you have to memorize them. As I said above, just be generally aware of what they are:

# 1. INITIAL ENROLLMENT PERIOD (IEP)

To get Medicare Part A and Part B, there's something called an Initial Enrollment Period, or IEP, that lasts for seven full months. This time period starts three months prior to your sixty-fifth birthday. It includes the month in which you turn age sixty-five, and it then runs for an additional three months afterward. During this time period, you can sign up (or passively accept) Original Medicare Parts A and B and sign up for any of the three different coverage paths.

For starters, most people get Medicare coverage automatically during this time, so there's nothing for you to do really but check your mailbox. These people include:

a.   People turning sixty-five who are already receiving benefits from Social Security or the Railroad Retirement Board.

b.   People under sixty-five with disabilities who have been receiving disability benefits for twenty-four months.

c.   People living with ALS (Amyotrophic Lateral Sclerosis) receive coverage the month their Social Security benefits start kicking in.

However, scenarios *do* exist where you'll have to proactively sign up for Medicare:

a.   People close to sixty-five and *not* receiving Social Security benefits.

b.   People living in Puerto Rico—they'll have to sign up for Part B separately.

If you're one of the folks that need to sign up, here's how this works:

Meet Jane. Jane's 65th birthday is June 22.

If Jane signs up for Medicare anytime in March, April, or May, her Medicare coverage will start June 1.

If Jane signs up for Medicare in June, her Medicare coverage will start July 1 (the very next month).

If Jane signs up in July, her Medicare coverage will start September 1 (2 months later!).

If Jane signs up in August, her Medicare coverage will start November 1 (3 months later!).

If Jane signs up in September, her Medicare coverage will start December 1 (3 months later!).

If Jane doesn't sign up for Part B at all during this time, she'll incur the dreaded Part B Late Enrollment Penalty, and she'll pay this penalty on top of her Part B premium for the rest of her life.

The age for receiving full Social Security benefits is ramping up to age sixty-seven. That means more and more people are falling into this category. They're eligible for Medicare at age sixty-five but have elected to defer Social Security until sometime after age sixty-five.

Want my advice? **If you fall into this category and need to actively sign up, do so as early as you can before your sixty-fifth birthday. That means three months prior to your birthday month. When you sign up for Original Medicare, *do not* cancel your prior insurance coverage until you get written confirmation with the dates of your coverage from Medicare.** You don't want to have a gap in coverage. I'd tell Jane to sign up in March. Don't mess around with it; just plan it out and get it done. If you have no insurance, then again, sign up for Medicare as soon as you're allowed.

*Besides, the earlier your Medicare coverage date starts, the earlier you can sign up for a Medicare Part D Prescription Drug Plan, Medicare Advantage plan, or Medicare Supplement plan. If you do it early, those coverages should start immediately when your Medicare parts A and B are effective.*

**I'm one of the folks that need to sign up. How do I do it?**

If you need to sign up, head over to this section of the Social Security website. Again, I'd do this as early as you can. Processing takes time, kind of like the DMV.

Here's how to do it.

**1** Enroll online. You can find the link and instructions on the website. Visit PrepareforMedicare.com/links or go directly to https://secure.ssa.gov/iClaim/rib (This is the fastest, easiest way to do it in my opinion.)

**2** Personally visit your local Social Security office. You can look for the physical Social Security offices online too. I've got them listed at PrepareforMedicare.com/links. They typically don't like or accept drop-ins, so make sure to get an appointment. There is no online scheduling feature, so you'll have to call first. They also don't encourage the in-person method of enrolling, so you might have to press them to agree to a meeting. Don't do this last-minute.

**3** Call Social Security and enroll over the phone. Be ready to wait and be ready for this to take an hour or more. Here's the phone number: 1-800-772-1213

Social Security offers a checklist of information you'll need to sign up for Medicare. You can find it here: PrepareforMedicare.com/links.

Remember, you'll most likely get Medicare Part A and B automatically.

## MEDICARE PART B LATE ENROLLMENT PENALTY

If you're eligible to get Medicare Part B, and you actively choose not to enroll in it for some reason, not only will you not have coverage for the items described earlier in the book, but if you ever do want to sign up for Part B, you'll get penalized for the *rest of your life*. You'll get charged an additional 10% higher Part B premium for every year you should or could have had Part B, but, for whatever reason, didn't.

If you defer enrolling in Part B because you're still working past age sixty-five and getting health insurance through your employer, *you won't be penalized for enrolling*. Once you stop working and want Medicare Part B, you can sign up then. The only situation in which you'll ever be penalized for not signing up for Medicare Part B is when you *should and could have but chose not to*. If you simply didn't want Medicare Part B for some reason but didn't have any other form of insurance, *then* wanted it later, you could still get it during the General Enrollment Period (starting on January 1 of each year), but you'll suffer the lifelong premium penalty.

## PART D LATE ENROLLMENT PENALTY

There's also a Medicare Part D late enrollment penalty. According to Medicare, the late enrollment penalty is an amount that's permanently added to your Medicare drug coverage (Medicare Part D) premium. You may owe a late enrollment penalty if, at any time after your Initial Enrollment Period is over, there's a period of *sixty-three or more days in a row when you don't have Medicare drug coverage or other creditable prescription drug coverage*. You'll generally have to pay the penalty for as long as you have Medicare drug coverage.

If you don't sign up for Medicare Part D when you're first allowed to do so, either through a Medicare Part D Prescription Drug plan or through a Medicare Advantage plan, you'll get financially penalized if you ever do decide to sign up. It's a good idea to sign up as soon as you're eligible, even though you may not use it. In fact, it's better than a really good idea. If you don't, that late enrollment financial penalty (higher premiums) will haunt you for the rest of your life. If you don't take any prescriptions, that's wonderful. Odds are, however, that at some point in your life, you will. Just get the cheapest Medicare Part D plan when you're eligible, so you are not haunted by the penalty for late enrollment. You can change your Part D Prescription Drug Plan and Medicare Advantage plan once per year under normal circumstances during the AEP. This means that even if you get the cheapest one initially because you're not taking any prescriptions, you can change once a year if your status changes.

Don't worry, just like Medicare Part B, you won't be penalized for not buying it if you're working past age sixty-five and have prescription drug coverage through your employer or elsewhere, but you'll have to prove it was "creditable" coverage to Medicare (as good as or better than Medicare Part D) when you do eventually sign up.

So, you'll want to sign up for Medicare Part B and get Medicare Part D coverage, either through a stand-alone Medicare Part D Prescription Drug Plan or a MAPD plan when you turn sixty-five. Right? Well, yes. Unless…

## WORKING PAST AGE SIXTY-FIVE

It's estimated that around 40% of people are now working past the "typical" retirement age of sixty-five, but by age seventy, most folks have stopped full-time work. So, if you're still working, you *can* defer signing up (and paying for) Medicare Part B until later and *not* get penalized when you eventually re-apply to get Medicare Part B. Here's what you need to be thinking about:

You're still working for an employer who has ***over twenty employees*** and are receiving health insurance benefits through your employer and want to keep it that way. Maybe your employer pays all of your premiums. Maybe your spouse or partner isn't eligible for Medicare yet, and you carry the insurance. In that case, you can "accept" Part A and defer enrollment in Part B. If this describes you, then you won't get a Part B penalty when you eventually retire and sign up, as long as you have "creditable coverage."

If you work for an employer that has *under twenty employees*, you'll have to get Medicare Part A and B when you're eligible. There are reasons for that, but they don't really matter to you, the consumer. Thus, it usually makes sense to drop your employer plan at that time while still working for the company because your employer-sponsored health insurance is usually way more expensive than Medicare Parts A and B and any other Medicare insurance plans you can layer on top of it. If you think your company is close to that twenty limit, check with the owner or their HR person to make sure.

**Wait, what if I carry the health insurance through my employer for my spouse or partner, and they're not eligible for Medicare yet?**

Well, you've got a decision to make. Keep working and providing employer-based health insurance, so your spouse or partner has coverage until they're eligible for Medicare, or stop working, take Medicare Part A and Part B, and buy your spouse or partner an Affordable Care Act Plan. You can shop your Affordable Care Act Plan options here: http://www.healthcare.gov.

Other than the scenarios above, it'll probably be much cheaper for you to continue working, drop your employer coverage, get Medicare Parts A and B, and sign up for other Medicare insurance on top of Original Medicare (Medicare Part D Prescription Drug Plan, a Medicare Advantage plan or a Medicare Supplement plan).

To Medicare, Creditable Coverage does not include COBRA coverage, certain retiree health plans, or VA coverage. ***Don't assume you've got creditable coverage and wait months before signing up for Part B. Fill out the application ASAP.***

If you've got an Affordable Care Act plan, you technically *can* keep it while on Medicare, but it probably won't make much financial sense for you to do so. That's because you won't get any premium tax credits or other cost savings, and you'll pay full price for it. If you have an ACA plan, there's a good overview and checklist to run through online if you think it might make sense. But, again, it probably doesn't make sense for the vast majority of people to keep an ACA plan when they get Medicare. If you want to run through the checklist, you can find it on the website at PrepareforMedicare.com/links.

Finally, some employers are now allowing the employee to get Medicare and still cover family members. This way, it's cheaper for the employer. There are always other exceptions and arrangements people make. Ask your HR department.

**Remember**—if you defer Part B or Part D enrollment, expect Medicare to ask you to prove you had coverage when you do eventually sign up for either. Don't throw away your paperwork. **Your HR department will have to give you a CMS-L564E form attesting that you did indeed have group health plan coverage. You can find that form on the website at PrepareforMedicare.com/links.**

When your employer-based group coverage ends, you will have eight months to enroll in Medicare Part B regardless of your age. If you don't do it within eight months, you'll get the dreaded penalty.

However, when you *do* eventually drop your employer coverage, **you only have sixty-three days to enroll in Medicare Part D prescription drug benefits,** either through a Medicare Advantage plan or a stand-alone Medicare Part D Prescription Drug Plan. *Therefore, it's extremely important to sign up for Part D and Part B and time it to occur during the first sixty days. That way, you're covered for both Medicare Part B and Medicare Part D.*

## 1.5 INITIAL COVERAGE ELECTION PERIOD (ICEP)

If you're deferring Part B for any reason, when you eventually do sign up for Medicare Part B, your election period code will most likely be the Initial Coverage Election Period or ICEP. I strongly urge you to use a Medicare insurance agent leading up to this decision and through the entire process. He or she should be able to help you not miss any deadlines.

Okay, I did my homework, understand the paragraphs above, and I want to defer Part B for a while. How do I do it?

Remember, for most of us, when you turn sixty-five, you'll get Medicare Part A automatically. You'll also get Medicare Part B automatically if you're drawing Social Security. However, if you don't want Medicare Part B, there's a form in the packet you get prior to age sixty-five that you can fill out that will allow you to defer Medicare Part B until a later date.

If you want to temporarily opt out of Part B until a later date, here's how to do it.

If your Medicare *hasn't started yet*, there are two ways to drop Part B:

**1** If you were automatically enrolled in both Part A and Part B and were sent a Medicare card, follow the instructions that come with the card and send the card back. If you keep the card, you keep Part B and will pay Part B premiums.

**2** If you signed up for Medicare through Social Security, contact Social Security. If your Medicare has started and you want to drop Part B, contact Social Security for instructions on how to submit a signed request. Your coverage will end the first day of the month after Social Security gets your request.

The phone number for Social Security is 800-772-1213. Again, if you want to go into a Social Security office, you can find one near you using their search tool. You can find that on the website, too, at PrepareforMedicare.com/links.

## 2. ANNUAL ELECTION PERIOD (AEP)

The AEP begins every year on October 15 and ends on December 7. This is why your mailbox, web browsers, and TV screens fill up with commercials and ads from insurance companies hoping to get you to buy or switch Medicare Advantage or Medicare Part D Prescription Drug Plans during this time period.

This is when you can change your Medicare Advantage plan or your Medicare Part D Prescription Drug Plan if you want. For instance, during the AEP, you can move from Original Medicare to Medicare Advantage or vice versa. You may also switch from one Medicare Advantage plan to another Medicare Advantage plan that may better suit your needs or your budget.

Likewise, you may also switch from one Medicare Part D Prescription Drug Plan to another, or you may join or leave a Medicare Part D plan altogether. Provided that you make any of these changes during the AEP, your new coverage will take effect on the following January 1, and your old one will immediately be dropped with no gap in coverage.

If you don't do anything or change anything, you just roll over and stay on the plan you have for the next year.

This does *not* apply to Medicare Supplement (Medigap) insurance. I'll cover those later in the book. But this period is *only* for changing Medicare Advantage Plans and Medicare Part D Prescription Drug Plans.

**Many authors and journalists mistakenly call the AEP "Open Enrollment" or "Annual Open Enrollment." It's not. It's the Annual Election Period. It bugs me that they get it wrong every year, and it's my book, so I'm pointing that out for my fellow scribes and readers. There are two distinct periods and mashing them into one is misleading and just factually incorrect. There is an Annual Election Period and an...**

# 3. OPEN ENROLLMENT PERIOD (OEP)

Although the Annual Election Period (AEP) ends on December 7 every year, that does not necessarily mean that you're completely out of luck if you still want to make a change after December 7. With the AEP occurring around the holidays, it's no wonder some folks simply miss it. Never fear, the OEP is here! During the Medicare Open Enrollment Period (OEP), some avenues could still allow you to make changes to your Medicare coverage without penalty and without having to wait until the AEP next year.

**It's also known as the Medicare Advantage Open Enrollment Period (MAOEP)**

The OEP runs from January 1st through March 31st every year. During this time, if you don't like the plan you bought, or something else changed between last year and this year, you can make a few changes. For example, let's say you didn't pay attention to the packet of plan changes your insurance company mailed to you in September, and you were surprised by a new, higher copay you had to pay at the pharmacy. Or maybe your doctor's copay went up, or they are no longer in your network. Now's the time to consider a change.

**During this time, you'll be able to:**

**1** Switch to a different Medicare Advantage plan.

**2** Drop your Medicare Advantage plan and return to Original Medicare, Part A and Part B. This means if you do this, you can use the OEP to sign up for a stand-alone Medicare Part D Prescription Drug Plan (again, *only* if you return to Original Medicare and go Bare-with-Medicare).

**3** Drop your stand-alone Medicare Part D Prescription Drug Plan. I can't think of a reason why you'd do that, but you can.

**What *can't* you do during the OEP?**

✔ Switch from Original Medicare to a Medicare Advantage plan.

✔ Switch from one stand-alone Medicare Part D Prescription Drug Plan to another.

If you decide to drop your Medicare Advantage plan and buy a Medicare Part D Prescription Drug plan during the OEP, you'll be bumped off of your Medicare Advantage plan and default back to Original Medicare A and B for your medical insurance coverage. I can't think of very many reasons why you'd do this, but I suppose if you really didn't like your Medicare Advantage plan and wanted to get rid of it, you could. As such, you may also need or want to purchase a Medicare Supplement insurance plan at that time. However, if that's your plan…

**Be Careful.**

I cover Medicare Supplement in depth in Chapter 4. However, since we're on the topic, I'll include some Medicare Supplement information here.

Depending upon the rules of your particular state, you may have to go through medical underwriting to purchase a Medicare Supplement plan outside of a special window when you turn sixty-five. Medicare Supplement plans are *not* like Original Medicare Parts A and B, Medicare Part D, or Medicare Part C (Medicare Advantage plans) in that Medicare Supplement insurance companies *can* deny you coverage based on your health.

 A Medicare Supplement policy is a separate policy from Original Medicare Parts A and B. Medicare Supplements are offered by Medicare Supplement insurance companies. These companies *can* deny you coverage or, at the very least, accept you but charge you a much higher premium. If you get denied coverage for a Medicare Supplement plan, you'll *only* have Original Medicare Parts A and B and a Medicare Part D Prescription Drug plan to fall back on, until the AEP (October 15-December 7th), when you can enroll in a Medicare Advantage plan once again. My advice is that if you want to go that way, you've got to apply and receive your acceptance or denial from the Medicare Supplement insurance company *before* you apply for a Medicare Part D Prescription Drug Plan and drop your Medicare Advantage plan.

### *Re-read the prior paragraph. It's important.*

In essence, you generally have a very small window to buy a Medicare Supplement plan with no medical questions to answer, and the Medicare Supplement insurance company must accept your enrollment. Said differently, Medicare Supplement plans have very narrow timeframes within which you can apply for coverage and not be subject to medical underwriting.

If you're on a Medicare Supplement already, be very, very sure you know what you're doing. Many people use a Medicare Supplement for a few years then move to a Medicare Advantage plan. Some people move from one Medicare Supplement plan to another to get a cheaper rate. **Whatever you do, don't drop a Medicare supplement plan** *before you get confirmation on your next insurance policy!*

 If you drop or cancel a Medicare Supplement plan, odds are, it'll be tough to get back on to it. If you drop your Medicare Advantage plan and go back to Original Medicare Parts A and B and a Medicare Part D Prescription Drug Plan, do not automatically assume you'll be able to buy a Medicare Supplement plan. This is unlike Medicare Part D Prescription Drug Plans or Medicare Part C Medicare Advantage plans. Again, those types of plans must accept you with no medical underwriting.

If you leave a Medicare Advantage plan during the OEP, your current Medicare Advantage coverage will remain in force until the end of the current month. Your new coverage will then take effect on the first day of the following month.

Please note, you can only make a change *one time* during the OEP. In other words, once you have made a change to your Medicare coverage using your OEP, that's it for the year. You may not go back in during this same time frame and make more changes.

Here's an example of what you *can't* do during the OEP. Let's say you move from a Medicare Advantage plan back to Original Medicare on February 1st and pick up a Medicare Part D Prescription Drug Plan to cover your prescription drugs.

That's it for the year. You're out of your OEP choices. Even if you change your mind, you cannot change your plan again on March 1 of the same year and go back into a Medicare Advantage plan. In that scenario, you'd have to wait until the AEP rolls around between October 15 and December 7.

That said, you better have a really good reason, and you better understand what benefits you will have in your new plan, as well as what you may be giving up, before switching plans—and from there, you can determine whether or not a change will truly be beneficial for you. The basic rule is this: *don't* drop Medicare Advantage in favor of a Medicare Supplement plus a Medicare Part D Prescription Drug Plan *before* you get accepted to enroll in a Medicare Supplement plan, if that's what you're planning to do. If you're okay with moving away from a Medicare Advantage plan and going back to Original

Medicare plus a Medicare Part D Prescription Drug Plan, you can do that during the OEP. If you want to change from your current Medicare Advantage plan and choose another one, you can do so—one time—during the OEP.

# 4. SPECIAL ENROLLMENT PERIODS (SEP)

Simply put, a Special Enrollment Period (SEP) lets you make changes to your Medicare Advantage plan or Medicare prescription drug plan coverage outside of the regular enrollment periods listed previously.

At last count, there are more than twenty-five types of SEPs. I'm not going to list all of them for the sake of sanity and brevity. If you have one or think you might have one that applies to your situation, here's where a good independent Medicare insurance agent comes in handy. You can also call a Medicare insurance company and ask. The telephone reps should know, but they might have to dig into their notes for a bit to find the answers. Again, even good Medicare insurance agents can't remember all of these off the top of their heads, but they do know where to find them and how to use them when these come up. I'd use an agent if you think you have some sort of event or extenuating circumstance outside of the IEP, AEP, and OEP that you need help with.

Here are a few of the more commonly used SEPs:

## MEDICARE ADVANTAGE "TRIAL PERIOD" SPECIAL ENROLLMENT PERIOD

People who enroll in a Medicare Advantage plan for the first time get a "trial period" (up to twelve months) to try out Medicare Advantage. If you do this and end up not liking the Medicare Advantage concept or plan, this SEP allows you to disenroll from your first Medicare Advantage plan and go back to Original Medicare. You'd get a "guaranteed issue right" to purchase a Medicare supplement plan without any type of underwriting. The Medicare Supplement companies have to accept you. This right lasts for sixty-three days after disenrollment from the MA plan, so, again, timing and planning are key here.

If you dropped a Medicare Supplement policy to join a Medicare Advantage plan for the first time, regardless of age, you also get a "trial period" (up to twelve months) to try it out. If you don't like it, you can go back to your Medicare supplement (up to 12 months) as well.

## RELOCATION SEP

This one is easy. It's a SEP you can use when you're on Medicare to change your Medicare Advantage or Medicare Part D Prescription Drug Plan if you permanently move. If you move across the street or usually within the same county, you probably won't qualify for this. But if you move out of your current county or state, you'll probably move out of the service area in which the insurance company operates. If you do this, you can sign up for either a new Medicare Advantage plan or Medicare Part D Prescription Drug Plan, depending on your situation.

## SEP FOR INSTITUTIONALIZED INDIVIDUALS

This one is for folks in nursing homes or residential long-term care facilities, some skilled nursing facilities, psychiatric hospitals, rehabilitation hospitals, long-term care hospitals, and swing beds. It allows you to enroll in or switch Medicare Advantage plans or Medicare Part D Prescription Drug Plan when you move into, reside in, or are discharged from certain long-term care facilities to join or disenroll from a Medicare Advantage plan. If you (or your loved one) qualify for this, you may join a Medicare Advantage plan or Medicare Part D Prescription Drug Plan, switch to a different Medicare Advantage plan, or disenroll from Medicare Advantage and go to Original Medicare.

## SEP FOR PEOPLE WITH LIMITED INCOME

There are a couple of these, and all of them revolve around whether or not you're eligible for one of the many special "financial help" programs offered by states and the federal government. See Chapter One for an overview, but generally speaking, if you make more than around $18,000 as an individual or under $30,000 as a couple per year, don't bother; you won't qualify.

I'm going to conclude this section the way I started it—the help, guidance, and assistance of a good Medicare insurance agent is a very good idea. I would not try to tackle anything myself outside of the IEP, AEP, and OEP. There's a lot you could potentially mess up or miss out on, and you definitely don't want to be in a position where you've missed important deadlines because you didn't understand the various election periods.

# MEDICARE STAR RATINGS

These days, it's hard to avoid seeing ratings everywhere you look. Consumer Reports has a star rating system. So does Google, JD Power, Morningstar, Yelp, and thousands of other industries and companies. Think about it. We've all been pre-conditioned to buy almost everything on a five-star rating system. Five means good, one means bad. Five is reserved for "awesome," and one reserved for "stay away."

Let's say you're buying a Bluetooth speaker on Amazon. You'd log into Amazon, type "Bluetooth speaker" in the search bar, and presto! Up pops hundreds of Bluetooth speakers. How on earth can you possibly sort through all of those Bluetooth speakers to find the best one?

Odds are, you first look at the price. Once you've narrowed your choices down that way, you're going to naturally go and look at how many stars it has. After all, the star rating on any Amazon product is left by Amazon customers like you. They've previously purchased the product and thought enough of it to come back to Amazon and rate it. If it's got four-and-a-half or higher stars, it makes you feel confident, right? It makes you feel like you'd be making a good purchase.

What if it's rated three-and-a-half stars? What if it's rated only three stars? Hmmm, you might pause a little bit and read user comments to see why it wasn't rated as high as four or five, right?

Well, there's a five-star rating system for Medicare, too. It's the federal government's attempt to tap into this idea to which we've all grown accustomed: a five-star rating system concept. This star rating system only applies to Medicare Advantage and Medicare Part D Prescription Drug Plans—Medicare Supplement plans are excluded.

The Medicare Star rating system is numbered from one to five, with five being the best and one being lowest in terms of quality of service:

- ✓ Five Stars—Excellent
- ✓ Four Stars—Above Average
- ✓ Three Stars—Average
- ✓ Two Stars—Below Average
- ✓ One Star—Poor

To determine these ratings, Medicare Advantage plans are rated in five different categories:

1. Staying healthy: screenings, tests, and vaccines

2. Managing chronic (long-term) conditions

3. Plan responsiveness and care

4. Member complaints, problems getting services, and choosing to leave the plan

5. Health plan customer service

Medicare Part D Prescription Drug Plans are rated in four different categories:

1. Drug plan customer service

2. Member complaints, problems getting services, and choosing to leave the plan

3. Member experience with the drug plan

4. Drug pricing and patient safety

## FIVE-STAR MEDICARE ADVANTAGE PLANS

Typically, highly integrated, strictly "staff model" HMO plans make up the majority of four-and-a-half or five-star plans. In other words, Medicare Advantage PPO and HMO models that offer more freedom of doctor choice, allow out-of-network access, and do not require referrals for you to see specific doctors, *tend* not to score four-and-a-half or five stars. These four-and-a-half or five-star HMOs usually have small networks aligned with a particular hospital or provider system. This is primarily because these companies can control their customer experiences from the time they step foot inside their doctor's office to when they're discharged from the hospital. From start to finish, these Medicare insurance companies integrate the customer experience within the doctor's offices, hospitals, and other network providers to strengthen clinical outcomes. This approach usually leads to very high satisfaction scores from customers.

If a Medicare insurance company achieves a five-star rating from Medicare, a few things happen. One, the Medicare insurance company gets additional monetary bonuses from Medicare. They get to keep some of the money, but most use the money to provide better insurance benefits or lower premiums for the plan. Second, five-star plans get a Special Enrollment Period (SEP) and can enroll Medicare consumers outside of the normal AEP and OEP windows. (This can only be used once between December 8 and November 30.)

For 2021, out of 800+ plans measured, only twenty-one earned five stars. You might think that would likely include only the big, brand-name companies, but you'd be wrong. The list includes smaller, state-based, or regional Medicare insurance companies like KelseyCare Advantage, Health Now New York, Martins Point, Kaiser Permanente, Tufts Health Plan, Health Partners, Capital District Physicians' Health Plan, Quartz Medicare Advantage of Wisconsin, and Health Sun. A few plans from the big brand-name companies made the list as well: UnitedHealthcare, CarePlus by Humana, Anthem BCBS, and Cigna. You can head over to PrepareforMedicare.com/links for the most recent list of five-star plans.

This goes to show that just because a company offers a smaller plan and doesn't spend a hundred million dollars in marketing every year, they can still put out a high-quality Medicare insurance product right alongside the larger national Medicare insurance companies!

## "TOO NEW TO RATE"

Sometimes, when you look at the star ratings, you'll run across Medicare Advantage plans and Medicare Part D Prescription Drug Plans that won't have a star rating; it'll say, "*Too New to Rate.*" For 2021, there were 417 of these available to buy.

Why would a product be rated *Too New to Rate*? Because it's either being offered for the first time or is under a year old. Thus, Medicare doesn't have enough data to measure the plan. It doesn't mean the Medicare insurance company who created the plan is necessarily new; it just means that particular plan is new. "Too New to Rate" usually gets a default star rating of three-and-a-half from Medicare, but you won't typically see that on Medicare.gov or the Medicare insurance company websites. That's just the default ranking those plans get behind the scenes for the first year.

### Medicare Star Rating Process—How Much Stock Should You Put In the Star Ratings?

First of all, the star ratings for plans you see on Medicare.gov and in plan documents for Medicare insurance companies are *at least a year old*. That's because the measurement periods don't line up very well with how Medicare Advantage and Medicare Part D Prescription Drug Plans are deployed. The lag can be as long as three years in some situations.

Second, Medicare changes the rules around how they score health plans every year. Think about it; there are over sixty-seven million people on Medicare. Can you really break down plan ratings across the country in only one way? Can you really break down these ratings into a neat five-star sliding scale? The obvious answer is no, and policy professionals and insurance companies quietly (and sometimes not so quietly) let Medicare know about it. Differences in geography, access to hospitals and doctors, income, and even attitudes about what it means to be healthy, mean the results are suspect and imperfect.

Here's another problem, and the difference between the Medicare star rating system and Amazon, Google, Yelp, and everyone else; the star ratings *are not based on direct consumer feedback. They're based on how Medicare and the federal government rate the Medicare insurance company plans,* with a little bit of direct consumer feedback sprinkled in. Medicare Advantage plans are rated on more than forty quality and performance measures, and Medicare Part D Prescription Drug Plans are rated on up to fourteen measures.

Like most attempts to aggregate lots of information into a small rating system for easy public consumption, it's not very clear how it affects the quality of your health insurance plan because there are so many data points Medicare monitors that don't apply to everyone on the same Medicare insurance plan. Yes, there's a component of consumer feedback, but most of the rating methodology is based on medical and prescription drug data.

But, in my opinion, there are some questions asked that are downright head-scratchers. Here are some I find particularly puzzling.

✔ In the last six months, how often did your health plan's customer service give you the information or help you needed? Answers can be Never, Sometimes, Usually, Always.

What if you didn't call customer service in the last six months? If you didn't, would you answer "never"? Never, by the way, is a negative score.

What if you couldn't remember what you did six months ago? (I personally couldn't even guess when I last called a customer service number.)

✔ In the last six months, how often did your health plan's customer service treat you with courtesy and respect? Answers can be Never, Sometimes, Usually, Always.

I don't know about you, but *my* version of what's courteous or respectful is probably going to be different than yours. And yours is going to be different than your neighbors'. Is that a fair way to measure Medicare insurance companies?

Have you had a flu shot since July 1?

Obviously, Medicare wants the answer to be yes (which is why they may ask). What if I don't *want* to get a flu shot? What if they make me feel bad? What if I have a fear of needles? If the answer is no, it counts as a negative mark against the Medicare insurance company. Is that fair?

 In the last six months, how often did you see the person you came to see within fifteen minutes of your appointment time? Answers can be Never, Sometimes, Usually, Always.

Have you ever been to the Emergency Room? Have you ever waited in your doctor's waiting room? Have you ever waited for more than fifteen minutes? And if you had to wait, what could your health insurance company do about it? You know the answer: nothing. No matter—if you answer negatively, it's a bad mark against the Medicare insurance plan.

## CHOOSE PLANS WITH THREE-AND-A-HALF STARS OR HIGHER

**My advice is this; plan star ratings should be one aspect of your Medicare insurance coverage decision. I'd urge you to not consider *any* Medicare Advantage or Part D Prescription Drug Plan lower than a three-and-a-half star rating.** However, the difference between three and three-and-a-half or the difference between three-and-a-half and four just isn't statistically significant. You probably won't know the difference. In my opinion, Medicare Star ratings shouldn't overshadow other considerations like premium, network, MOOP (Maximum-out-of-Pocket, addressed in the next chapter), or your prescription drug coverage.

**That said, star ratings *are important to you* because ultimately, if your plan is rated three stars or below, it generally means you'll pay more money for your policy, or your benefits won't be as rich as plans with four stars or higher.** This is because Medicare insurance companies get bonuses and rebates from the federal government for higher star ratings. When they get this bonus money, they have to spend much of it to improve the insurance benefits or lower the monthly premiums for the Medicare insurance plan. So, if you have a four-star rated plan, odds are you have better benefits available to you as compared to a two-star rated plan.

That's another reason why I recommend you consider *only* three-and-a-half star or higher rated Medicare insurance plans. A low star score is generally thought of as having a two-and-a-half or below. If a plan consistently scores at two-and-a-half stars or below, Medicare will add a "low performing plan" indicator on Medicare's own website. It looks like an upside-down triangle with an exclamation point and often limits enrollment from the Medicare website. In fact, people who are on plans that get this "low performing plan" status get letters in the mail from Medicare informing them of the performance of the company. Not good if you're an insurance company, and not good if you're on that plan!

Do star ratings really matter? Sure. They matter because they give an overall indication as to the quality and customer experience of a given Medicare Advantage plan or Medicare Part D Prescription Drug Plan. Is there a significant difference between a three-star plan and a four-star plan from the consumer's standpoint or experience? Probably not. There are flaws, to be sure, and the rules insurance companies must abide by change every year. The real impact to *you*, the *consumer*, is that higher-performing plans are paid more by the federal government per person enrolled. Most of that additional money must be put back into benefits or lower insurance policy premiums, which, in the long run, is better for you and your wallet.

CHAPTER THREE

# THE FOUR
# "FRUSTRATING FLAWS"
# OF ORIGINAL MEDICARE

Now that you have a decent idea of what's covered under each Parts A, B, C, and D of Medicare, before we move on we should discuss a point I made in the preceding chapters a few times. I'll put this out there right now—if you decide to stay on Original Medicare Parts A and B for your health insurance coverage, there are some things you should know.

Remember, I call sticking with Original Medicare Parts A and B for your healthcare coverage going "Bare-with-Medicare."

In my opinion, there are four Frustrating Flaws with Original Medicare, and I briefly mentioned three already in the previous chapters. They are:

**1** No MOOP (Annual Maximum Out Of Pocket)

**2** Medicare Part B Excess Charges

**3** Coverage Limitations

**4** Medicare.gov website limitations

The first three have to do with the way Original Medicare insurance benefits are constructed. That is, how Original Medicare Parts A and B work or don't work—what's covered and what's not. The fourth one, the Medicare.gov website limitations, really frustrates a lot of Medicare consumers. The Plan Finder feature on Medicare.gov is meant to be a one-stop shopping tool for everyone on Medicare, but it has a lot of flaws which I address.

Let's start with number one.

## ORIGINAL MEDICARE FRUSTRATING FLAW NUMBER ONE

### MOOP

**What's a MOOP? Any insurance professional will tell you, at its core, an insurance product should provide financial protection for you and your family and heirs from catastrophic events. In other words, insurance, at a bare minimum, should shield you from bankruptcy and financial ruin.** In every other personal insurance I can think of, there's always, *always*, something called a MOOP, which is a Maximum Out Of Pocket clause. These are either episodic or annual. But basically, a MOOP is financial protection should you have a bad health year accompanied by very expensive medical bills. It limits how much money—worst case scenario—you'd have to pay out of your pocket during a year. In insurance-speak, these are also called Annual Maximums, stop-loss amounts, annual plan maximums, or some other variation of those terms, but the concept is the same. Once you spend a certain amount, you're done paying out of your pocket, and the insurance company covers 100% beyond that amount.

Let's say you get cancer. You're in and out of the hospital; you're seeing multiple doctors, undergoing chemotherapy, using very expensive injectable drugs, and doing physical therapy over the course of several months. I've seen many examples of cancer treatments running bills well over $1,000,000 in just a few months.

When you have (or had) medical insurance through your employer, those plans typically come with deductibles, coinsurance amounts, and co-pays. But after you pay a certain amount of money towards these in a given year, you stop paying, and the insurance company pays 100%. These days, most come with a MOOP of $2,000-$5,000 for individuals and anywhere between $5,000 to $10,000 for family coverage if you have that.

Even if you were on an individual Affordable Care Act plan (aka ACA, ObamaCare, or a Marketplace Plan), the out-of-pocket limit for a marketplace plan can't be more than $8,550 for an individual and $17,100 for a family in 2021.

Original Medicare doesn't do that. I don't know why. It doesn't make any sense why it doesn't. It just doesn't have a MOOP. If you've got Original Medicare and no other Medicare insurance on top of that or in place of that, you have no annual or lifetime cap on how much you could pay. There's simply no limit to how much you can be charged if you get really sick and you only have Original Medicare, which is why many people buy other Medicare insurance.

Think about it. It doesn't make any sense. When you buy homeowner's insurance and your house burns down, you typically pay your deductible, and the insurance company pays 100% of the cost of replacement or re-build.

When you buy car insurance and total your car, you'll usually pay your deductible, then the insurance company pays for a new one or cuts you a check for 100% of its residual value.

In other words, insurance in those situations limits your maximum out-of-pocket responsibility to a certain dollar amount or a certain percentage. I can't come up with any other examples in the wild, wonderful world of insurance where there's simply no cap—no limit on the amount of out-of-pocket you could potentially be on the hook for except if you stay on Original Medicare Parts A and B with no additional medical insurance like a supplement or Medicare Advantage.

Let's revisit a scenario from earlier. If you're Bare-with-Medicare and hospitalized for 100 days, you'll owe around $15,000 just for that. Once discharged, you have to do forty days in a Skilled Nursing Facility. The quick math there is 19 days X $176 = $3,344 + $1,408 for a total of $19,888. Then, of course, there are going to be follow-up doctors' visits for which you must pay your annual Medicare Part B deductible plus 20% of each doctor's visit, prescription drugs you must take . . . the list goes on. It's not too hard to see how a bad health event that requires a long hospital stay could end up with you owing your hospitals and doctors more than $50,000.

That example doesn't even factor in the cost of items that aren't covered by Original Medicare, such as eyewear, dental procedures, your Part D prescription costs, etc. And those don't even count towards the MOOP if you're Bare-with-Medicare.

How likely is it that you'll be in the hospital for one hundred days? Highly unlikely. It's more likely that (a) you'll be dead or (b) you'll be moved out to a nursing home or a Skilled Nursing Facility (SNF). Not trying to be morbid, just realistic.

How likely are you to stay for forty days in an SNF? Not likely for the same reasons.

How likely are you to have multiple doctors' visits and multiple medications after being discharged from the hospital or the SNF? Pretty likely.

I've looked and looked, but I can't find any resource that tells me what percentage of people on Bare-with-Medicare got hit with, say, more than $20,000 in medical bills. If you know, send me an email. I'd love to learn about it. My smart actuary friends in the insurance industry have told me it's probably 1% of the population.

One percent? Sounds safe . . . until you do the math. Let's say 25% of the people eligible for Medicare go with Bare-with-Medicare for their medical insurance. In other words, they don't have a Medicare Advantage plan or a Medicare Supplement plan. Twenty-five percent of the sixty-seven million people on Medicare is 16.75 million people. One percent of that population is 167,500 people. So, if that 1% number is true, you're looking at three NFL football stadiums full of people who could certainly use a MOOP. Are you willing to risk it? I'm not.

Look. How much financial protection you need is up to your personal risk tolerance, health status, and the thickness of your wallet. I think it's safe to say that most people shouldn't be purchasing super-rich insurance products that offer first-dollar coverage if they don't fit into their budget. That is, of course, unless you simply like the peace of mind paying a lot of monthly premium up-front in return for largely first-dollar insurance coverage. **It's all about your personal risk tolerance and funds available; do you not mind paying more in monthly premium even if you never use the benefits? Or would you rather keep the majority of those premiums in your wallet and face more cost-sharing if and when you do use the insurance product?**

You want a MOOP? All Medicare Advantage plans must have a MOOP for medical, and none have one higher than $7,550 in-network and $11,000 outside of the network (for PPO plans) annually in 2021 and 2022. The popular Medicare Supplement plans (F and C, G and N) also limit your MOOP.

Don't care about the MOOP? Like the idea of self-insuring? Have plenty of dough in the bank as a hedge against this, admittedly, worst-case scenario? Fine. Going Bare-with-Medicare isn't for everyone, but it's a solution that has worked for millions of Medicare beneficiaries since the 1960s!

Odds are that you'll never come close to being in the hospital for more than twenty days in any one stay, and it's highly unlikely you'll be in a Skilled Nursing Facility for more than ten days. True, these are a few hypothetical, worst-case scenarios, but it still doesn't make up for the fact that you're financially exposed to real, catastrophic medical bills if you stick with Original Medicare and don't add additional insurance coverage.

*The major drawback* to going Bare-with-Medicare by staying on Original Medicare Plans A and B only for your medical insurance coverage is that it doesn't have a MOOP expense, and it's the **primary reason I think you should buy a Medicare Supplement plan or a Medicare Advantage plan. It's not mandatory, and plenty of people don't. But I highly suggest you do.**

Today, approximately 25% of all people on Medicare go Bare-with-Medicare and stick with Original Medicare for their health insurance coverage. Knowing what I know, I certainly wouldn't, especially without a MOOP. By going Bare-with-Medicare, you're opening yourself up to the potential for financial ruin if you have a bad (or several bad) health year (Sources: PrepareforMedicare.com/sources).

# ORIGINAL MEDICARE FRUSTRATING FLAW NUMBER TWO

## MEDICARE PART B EXCESS CHARGES

What are excess charges? Well, first, let's briefly outline how doctors get paid if you have Original Medicare (Medicare Advantage is different).

The vast majority of doctors and hospitals across the country accept what's called "Medicare Assignment." In plain English, that means Medicare says they'll pay the doctors and hospitals a certain amount for a procedure or a doctor's visit, and those doctors and hospitals essentially say, "Okay." These folks are then "participating" in Medicare. In return, they're not allowed to bill the patient any additional amounts over the deductibles and coinsurance necessary under Original Medicare. If a doctor, hospital, or other facility does *not* accept Medicare Assignment (non-participating), they can still bill Medicare, get paid that same amount outlined by Medicare, and then bill *you* an additional 15% above and beyond what Medicare paid them. This is called the Medicare Excess Charge. Yes, Medicare allows this. Of course, doctors and hospitals that opt out of Medicare altogether can bill you whatever they want.

The excess charges only apply to physicians or items billed under Medicare Part B.

Eight states have laws prohibiting Medicare Part B excess charges:

- ✔ Connecticut
- ✔ Minnesota
- ✔ Ohio
- ✔ Pennsylvania
- ✔ Rhode Island
- ✔ Vermont

✓ Massachusetts

✓ New York

The financial exposure to excess charges is an oft-cited reason Medicare insurance agents and companies use to sell certain types of Medicare Supplement plans. Some Medicare Supplement plans cover the potential 15% upcharge for Medicare Part B excess, and of course, usually charge higher premiums for plans that cover this possibility. Medicare Advantage plans don't normally have to deal with this because they don't allow excess charges to be billed for providers in their networks and will usually cover them if you have a PPO and decide to go out of network.

While yes, it is a fact this exists, and I believe this to be a Frustrating Flaw of Original Medicare, **I'm here to tell you, it's probably not that big of a deal,** especially if you don't see a psychiatrist. Why?

Before you get all worried about these charges, it's important to put them in perspective. Over 99% of doctors and hospitals across the country accept Medicare Assignment. The notable exception is psychiatrists (7%) (Sources: PrepareforMedicare.com/sources).

Like I said above, if you happen to run into a doctor that won't accept Medicare assignment, they can charge you 15% more for the service. Doesn't sound like a big deal until you start talking about multiple visits for, say, cancer. And there's no limit to the number of times that doctors can charge you the additional fee. It's not like it's just a one-time deal.

The Kaiser Family Foundation noted that the more troubling statistic isn't that Medicare providers are opting out of Medicare, it's that they aren't accepting new patients.

"... *some physicians are not accepting any new patients, including patients with Medicare and private insurance (i.e., closed practices). Past analysis found that 21% of non-pediatric primary care physicians accept Medicare but are not taking any new Medicare patients, as compared to 14% who are not taking new patients with commercial insurance.*" (Sources: PrepareforMedicare.com/sources).

Again, if you live in Connecticut, Minnesota, Ohio, Pennsylvania, Rhode Island, Vermont, Massachusetts, or New York, never fear! They've outlawed this practice. However, in the rest of the states, doctors—including surgeons and specialists—are allowed to charge that additional 15% more than the Medicare-approved amount for medical procedures. So, how do you fix this?

Only two Medicare Supplement plans cover Medicare excess charges, and one of them is no longer available for people who turned sixty-five on or after January 1, 2020. People who turned sixty-five before that date may still have access to this plan called Medicare Supplement Plan F. The other is Medicare Supplement Plan G, which is essentially the new replacement for Medicare Supplement Plan F now that it's going away for people who turn sixty-five after 2020. The only difference between the two is that Plan F covers the Medicare Part B deductible. Plan G does not.

The other option? Get a Medicare Advantage plan. You don't have to worry about the Medicare Assignment question because the insurance companies contract providers who already accept Medicare Assignment. Even if you have a Medicare Advantage plan that allows you to go outside of the insurance company's network, such as a PPO or an HMO-POS plan, you most likely won't get charged Medicare Part B Excess Charges. If you have questions, call your Medicare insurance company.

Is it worth a few extra bucks in premiums to get a Medicare Supplement plan that covers these excess charges? I'd say yes. Medicare Supplement Plan G is the only one that covers these, and it's the most popular, best-selling Medicare Supplement plan you can currently buy. If you already have a Medicare Supplement Plan F (again, no longer able to be sold if you became eligible for Medicare after January 1, 2020), that covers the Medicare Part B excess charges, too.

# ORIGINAL MEDICARE FRUSTRATING FLAW NUMBER THREE

## COVERAGE LIMITATIONS

We already know Original Medicare doesn't cover Long-Term Care (LTC). That's a huge coverage gap. Medicare only pays for stays in Skilled Nursing Facilities, hospice, physical therapy, occupational therapy, and in-home speech-language pathology in certain circumstances, but won't pay for anything long-term. Benefits for nursing home and home health services are limited. Most Long-Term Care services assist people with Activities of Daily Living (ADLs), such as dressing, bathing, and using the bathroom. Long-Term Care can be provided at home or in a facility. You'd have to buy a separate Long-Term Care insurance policy or some type of life insurance with LTC benefits attached to it to insure yourself for coverage that includes medical and non-medical care for Long-Term Care to meet health or personal needs.

Besides not covering LTC, there are quite a few healthcare-related items that Original Medicare Parts A and B don't cover. Here's the list from Chapter One again.

1. Retail prescription drugs (these are covered under Part D)

2. Custodial care (help with bathing, dressing, using the bathroom, and eating)

3. Private hospital room or private nursing in the hospital

4. Long-Term Care (nursing homes, retirement homes, and assisted living)

5. Cosmetic surgery

6. Most chiropractic services when not medically necessary

7. Most care while traveling outside the United States

**8** Healthy food dollar amount allowances at grocery stores

**9** Adult Daycare visits and home helpers

**10** Lifestyle drugs, including erectile dysfunction prescriptions

**11** Air conditioner allowances for people with COPD and asthma

**12** Transportation to doctor's appointments

**13** Nutritional programs, personal trainers, and access to spas

**14** Grocery delivery

**15** Over-the-counter allowances

**16** Acupuncture and massage

**17** Gym memberships or fitness classes

**18** Weight management programs

**19** Dental insurance and dentures

**20** Routine eye exams and glasses

**21** Routine hearing tests and hearing aids

**22** Foreign travel

As a result, Medicare Supplement plans, since they only fill in the deductible and coinsurance gaps of what Original Medicare covers, don't (typically) cover any of the items on this list.

Many Medicare Advantage plans *do* cover these items, however, and, in my opinion, this is why they've exploded in popularity over the last ten years. I've yet to find a Medicare Advantage plan that covers cosmetic surgery or Long-

Term Care. However, for a number of years, there have been plenty of Medicare Advantage plans out there that come with dental, vision, gym memberships, and hearing benefits.

**This is what sets Medicare Advantage plans apart from their cousins, the Medicare Supplements. You can actually use your Medicare Advantage plan when you're *not* sick.**

In 2019, Medicare redefined what Medicare Advantage plans could potentially offer and opened up the floodgates of what insurance companies may offer on top of traditional medical and prescription drug benefits. That's why you'll find some Medicare Advantage plans offering coverage for at least some of those items found above. Sometimes, those benefits aren't easily (or at all) displayed on Medicare's website, or even the insurance company's website, so you'll have to do some digging to find the plans that offer these additional benefits. If you find a good Medicare insurance agent in your area, they'll most likely know which plans offer these additional built-in features and benefits. They can help you decide whether or not a given plan is a good fit for you. But Medicare Advantage plans with a long list of additional benefits are out there, even though it might take a little effort to find them. I cover Medicare insurance agents later in the book, but a good quality Medicare insurance agent can help you find the best plan for you.

Do you need all of these? Any of these? Isn't the whole point of Medicare insurance to cover you for medical and prescription drug coverage? Sure. But if there are options out there to get that coverage plus additional benefits, why not at least explore it? While many Medicare Advantage plans cover these additional benefits, Original Medicare does not. Most Medicare Supplement plans don't either.

## TRAVEL BENEFITS

Before we move on to the next section, let's briefly talk about travel and Medicare.

Just to clarify, we're not talking about spending a month with your grandkids a state away, nor are we talking about being a snowbird. If you summer in Chicago and winter in Phoenix, you need to buy an insurance policy using the address that Social Security has on file as your place of residence. In other words, your official address needs to be the place in which you spend the majority of your time when you're applying for your Medicare insurance coverage.

This section specifically addresses utilizing your benefits while traveling within the U.S. and other countries. If you go the Medicare Advantage route, many of them have travel benefits.

If you are Bare-with-Medicare and using Original Medicare Parts A and B with a Medicare Part D Prescription Drug Plan, your benefits travel with you throughout the fifty states and U.S. territories (District of Columbia, Puerto Rico, the U.S. Virgin Islands, Guam, the Northern Mariana Islands, and American Samoa).

Traveling overseas or on a cruise ship gets trickier.

The Medicare website on travel offers an easy explanation that isn't 100% complete, nor does it do a very good job of highlighting when you're not covered while traveling if you're Option #1 Bare-with-Medicare. I've pasted an excerpt from the webpage below for your convenience.

> Medicare may pay for inpatient hospital, doctor, ambulance services, or dialysis you get in a foreign country in these rare cases:
>
> You're in the U.S. when a medical emergency occurs, and the foreign hospital is closer than the nearest U.S. hospital that can treat your medical condition.
>
> You're traveling through Canada without unreasonable delay by the most direct route between Alaska and another state when a medical emergency occurs, and the Canadian hospital is closer than the nearest U.S. hospital that can treat the emergency.
>
> You live in the U.S. and the foreign hospital is closer to your home than the nearest U.S. hospital that

can treat your medical condition regardless of whether
an emergency exists.

In some cases, Medicare Part B (Medical Insurance)
may cover medically necessary health care services
you get on board a ship within the territorial waters
adjoining the land areas of the U.S. Medicare won't pay
for health care services you get when a ship is more
than six hours away from a U.S. port.

Medicare drug plans don't cover prescription drugs
you buy outside the U.S.

Clear as mud, right? There's a zinger right there at the end! Did you miss it? Here it is again. **Medicare drug plans don't cover prescription drugs you buy outside the U.S.**

Prescription drugs purchased overseas are never covered by Medicare Part D. That means your Medicare Part D benefits either within an MAPD plan or a Medicare Part D Prescription Drug Plan are worthless overseas. Better stock up before you go. I must say, it's also interesting to see that if you go on a cruise, you better only get sick if you're close to the U.S. or one of its territories. Here's one more item of note from the site.

Foreign hospitals aren't required to file Medicare
claims. If you're admitted to a foreign hospital under
one of the situations above, and if that hospital doesn't
submit Medicare claims for you, you need to submit an
itemized bill to Medicare for your doctor, inpatient,
and ambulance services.

This is where having an additional travel insurance plan is helpful.

If you're Bare-with-Medicare and get sick overseas, you'll very likely have to pay either with cash or credit card for your health care at the time of service. You'll then have to take all of the paperwork home with you and fill it out. There are potentially nine forms you will need to fill out. If you want your son or daughter to help out, they need to fill out a form too. You better do it as soon as you get home; if you wait more than twelve months to file the paperwork, it could be denied by Medicare.

You can head to the website to read it yourself if you'd like. PrepareforMedicare.com/links.

If you are Bare-with-Medicare, it's a smart idea to buy short-term travel health insurance if you travel overseas. That's my personal opinion, of course, and I show you how to shop for that below.

What if you have a Medicare Advantage plan or a Medicare Supplement? I'm so glad you asked.

## TRAVEL WITHIN THE UNITED STATES

If you're on a Medicare Supplement plan, you're in luck! Medicare Supplement plans don't come with network restrictions. That means you can essentially go to any doctor anywhere you'd like across the country. If you're on a Medicare Advantage HMO (Health Maintenance Organization) plan, you may be out of luck if you get sick, even in the next ZIP code.

An MAPD HMO plan has a defined service area (usually by county), and there are next to zero out-of-network benefits. For example, if you have a small, strict gatekeeper HMO model Medicare Advantage plan with a limited service area around where you live in Sarasota, Florida, forget getting routine care while on your visit with the kids in Denver, Colorado. That is, of course, unless there's an emergency. There's always ER coverage for emergencies wherever you are. Aside from what the government mandates that HMO plans must include in their coverage (covering care for emergencies out of your area), most do not have what you'd normally consider "travel" coverage. To get the skinny, you need to pull out your Summary of Benefits booklet for your policy or call the company and ask. You can find more detailed information in the Evidence of Coverage.

If you have a Medicare Advantage PPO (Preferred Provider Organization) plan, those by design have out-of-network coverage if you're traveling out of your service area in the U.S.. Often, it's covered, but at the out-of-network rate and will cost you more than if you would have stayed in their network. This is one of the nice features of Medicare Advantage PPO plans. The out-of-network MOOP will be higher than your in-network MOOP, so be aware of that. Many Medicare Advantage PPO plans have national networks—which means you can potentially stay in network outside of your state. This can be a big deal if you're a snowbird or visit family outside of your home state or area for extended periods. Not all Medicare Advantage PPOs have this feature. So, again, ask your Medicare insurance agent or a phone representative about it if it's important to you.

Many Medicare Advantage companies tack on additional travel features to their plans to include some sort of U.S. travel coverage to address this. They vary from company to company. Alternatively, some Medicare Advantage plans allow you to use in-network providers in other states. But you might have to call the insurance company and tell them you're traveling, so they can make a note in your account. It all depends on the insurance company's policies and procedures; there's no one solution across the board. The details exist; you'll just have to dig through the Summary of Benefits and the Evidence of Coverage to find them. You can also call the company or ask your Medicare insurance agent to explain it as it applies to your particular question or situation.

## INTERNATIONAL TRAVEL COVERAGE

Not all Medicare Advantage plans cover international travel. If they do, they only cover very specific events like using an Urgent Care or Emergency Room. If this is a deal-breaker or a decision point you need to know more about, you can either spend hours digging through plan documents (these items are found in the Evidence of Coverage) or call the insurance company's customer service number and ask them to read it to you. You can also use and ask an expert independent Medicare insurance agent.

If you have a Medicare Supplement plan, you're in luck, my friend. Medicare Supplement Plans C, D, F, G, M, and N provide foreign travel emergency health care coverage when you travel outside the U.S., and Plans C, D, E, F, G, H, I, J, M, and N pay 80% of the billed charges for certain medically-necessary emergency care outside the U.S. after you meet a $250 deductible for the year. These Medicare Supplement policies cover foreign travel emergency care if it begins during the first sixty days of your trip and if Medicare doesn't otherwise cover the care. The lifetime limit on this is $50,000. You can find a chart of what all the Medicare Supplement plans cover on the website at PrepareforMedicare.com/links.

So, what are your other options? How can you be sure? **Personally, if I'm going on an offshore cruise or overseas for any length of time, I'm buying a separate policy.** You can buy overseas travel medical insurance if you have a Medicare Advantage plan, a Medicare Supplement, or are Bare-with-Medicare with a Medicare Part D Prescription Drug Plan. All you have to do is Google "ex-pat medical insurance," and you'll find many brand-name health insurance carriers that have plans you can buy. There's little chance your local Medicare health insurance agent will sell these plans, so the internet is your friend here. I'd recommend you skip the ads and go to the organic search results under them. Some of these insurance policies have pre-existing condition limits and waiting periods, so plan accordingly. I put a few links on the website for you: PrepareforMedicare.com/links.

# ORIGINAL MEDICARE FRUSTRATING FLAW NUMBER FOUR

## MEDICARE.GOV WEBSITE LIMITATIONS

If you're on Medicare and use the internet to look at insurance plan options, Medicare.gov is the most-visited website in the country. It's for good reason. It's a government site preferred by search engines, which is why it normally pops up in first position (after the ads, of course) when you search for terms containing "Medicare." Medicare.gov doesn't come with sales pitches or many annoying pop-ups (although they do have a few) asking you to click-to-chat or call in and talk to a sales agent. It shows all of the plans in your area, whereas most other insurance sales websites do not. It doesn't give the sense of providing preferential treatment or recommendations for one insurance company over the other. It also doesn't give any sales spin to the information it provides. It does provide links to hundreds of important documents.

You can find a *ton* of information there, some of which I reference in these pages and others I've stuck in the back of the book for you to peruse. However, all that information is part of the problem, in my opinion. Navigation is difficult. The website is not organized in a user-friendly way. Nor is it very reader-friendly. In short, it operates and reads like a government website.

You can sign up for Medicare Part D Prescription Drug Plans and Medicare Advantage plans through this site, and they list all of the options available to you—not just the ones that an insurance agent or an online insurance agency wants you to see, which is good. Medicare.gov does most of this pretty well. It's great for finding a Medicare Part D Prescription Drug Plan. We'll cover how to do this in Chapter Nine, but, briefly, if you go to Medicare.gov and click "Find Health & Drug Plans" right on the homepage, it'll take you to the Plan Comparison tool. When it takes you through several steps, it does a good job of allowing you to enter your prescriptions and find your local pharmacy. It will then spit out options for you based upon your current prescriptions and the pharmacy you picked, defaulting to the selection of "Lowest Drug + Premium Cost." You can also sort by "Lowest Yearly Drug Deductible" and "Lowest Monthly Premium." You can even compare a few side-by-side. Find one that works for you, and you can click right through and enroll right on your computer. Fantastic!

Well, hold on a second. While it may show all of the plans available to you, and it's convenient for shopping Medicare Part D Prescription Drug Plans, there are a few flaws I need to mention.

**It's not so great for finding a Medicare Advantage plan and even worse for finding a Medicare Supplement plan to meet your needs.**

First of all, if you're using Medicare.gov to buy a Medicare Part D Prescription Drug Plan or a Medicare Advantage plan, the site uses an algorithm to rank plans for you. The problem is, you and I don't know the algorithm. If you sort by lowest drug and premium cost, it looks like it filters it by the in- and out-of-network medical deductibles, which are higher than just the in-network deductibles. Well, I suppose the algorithm is assuming people are going in and out of network? Why does it do that? I didn't even enter my doctors into the tool because the website won't let me. How do they know I'm going out of network if they don't know my doctors? It's all very confusing. Does it place a higher priority on Medicare Star Ratings? MOOP? Prescription drug deductibles? We don't know. I don't know. It's all a mystery.

And about those star ratings . . . I'm glad they show them for this year, but what about last year? What about three years ago? How can I tell if this plan's star ratings have been going up, going down, or staying the same? Has the plan's star ratings been improving or getting worse over time? Medicare.gov doesn't show that.

If you're looking at Medicare Part D Prescription Drug Plans, you *can* see a list of pharmacies. That's a great thing. But (and this is a *big but* and the #1 reason this is a Frustrating Flaw) if you're looking at Medicare Advantage plans, you cannot look up your providers on Medicare.gov. You have zero ability to enter your doctors and preferred hospitals in Medicare.gov. To do that, you have to visit each insurance company's website and look them up yourselves. And let me tell you, not only is that difficult (multiple plans, multiple networks to wade through), but it's extremely time-consuming.

When you look at a plan, it says, "Estimated Total Lowest Drug + Premium Cost." In other words, it's not exact. How accurate is it? We really don't know.

Medicare.gov doesn't tell you whether or not the plan is relatively new or how long it's been around. Do you want to buy a plan that's been around for a decade? Or only two years? We can't tell, and plans come and go all the time. I want to know that whatever plan I'm choosing stands a good chance of being around for a few years.

Medicare.gov doesn't tell you whether the plan benefits went up or down year after year. Did the copays, deductibles, and coinsurance amounts for your medical and drug coverage for the plan you're considering get better from the prior year, or did they get worse? I'd like to know which direction the benefits are heading year-after-year before I buy. As a general rule of thumb, plan benefits get worse, and premiums go up when insurance companies start losing money on a particular plan. They stay the same or get better when they're making money on the plan. If insurance companies lose money on a plan over multiple years, it's a pretty good bet the benefits will continue to get worse, premiums may go up, or they may stop offering the plan altogether and force you to find another health plan.

Medicare.gov doesn't tell you how many people are enrolled in the plan. I know it may not matter to some, but isn't there a little safety in numbers here? Wouldn't you like to know that other people on Medicare seem to be okay having this plan? Wouldn't you prefer joining a plan that has, say, 100,000 people on it, and not just ten? It's much easier for an insurance company to cancel an insurance plan that only has ten people on it.

Medicare.gov shows those great "other" plan benefits that can come with a Medicare Advantage plan—and it'll list them right on the page. But it does not tell you any specifics about that coverage. Even if you click on the Plan Details button and scroll all the way through, you simply cannot find meaningful details. For example, it might show that the Medicare Advantage plan covers dental, but is there an allowance? Is there an annual amount you're able to spend? Is that annual amount different for what's called routine versus comprehensive? Must you use a specific network of dentists, or are you free to see any dentist? Must you pay for your care up-front then file with the insurance company for reimbursement? Or will the insurance company pay the claim for you? You simply can't find this important information on Medicare.gov.

The same can be said about many of those other plan benefits that accompany Medicare Advantage plans. For example, is there an annual over-the-counter medicine spending allowance? How much is it? Can you use it once a year, once a quarter, or once a month? There just aren't any specifics listed, and to get them, you're going to have to dig into each insurance company's website or talk to a professional Medicare insurance agent who knows what they're doing and where to find this information (which many people do).

Yes, there are a few more:

Medicare.gov doesn't provide any options to plug in your health status. Are you sick? Do you see your doctors thirty times a year or only three times? That will certainly affect your estimated annual drug and healthcare costs.

Medicare.gov doesn't hide MA-only plans which do *not* come with a Medicare Part D benefit embedded and are really only good for about ten million Americans who are veterans. Yes, you can accidentally enroll in one of these plans if you're not careful. If you do, you won't have prescription drug benefits. On Medicare.gov, these plans look almost exactly like regular Medicare Advantage plans that come with a Medicare Part D plan embedded in them (MAPD plans). They don't put up a little flag or use a different font—nothing at all to indicate the plan is an MA-only plan and not an MAPD. All they do is add this line. *"This plan doesn't cover prescription drugs, so you'll pay for the drug's full cost under this plan. Other Medicare Advantage plans offer drug coverage."* Wow. If you enroll in one of these and don't mean to, oh boy—what a mess you've just made.

Medicare.gov is also almost useless when it comes to helping you buy a Medicare Supplement plan. Sure, it'll let you enter your age, sex, and whether you use tobacco or not, but not much else. It doesn't allow you to compare company prices like you can when buying Medicare Advantage or Medicare Part D Prescription Drug Plan. When you enter that information, it takes you to a screen to show you all the Medicare Supplement plans available in your area. If you click on one, it takes you to a screen that simply links to insurance company websites. Often, those links just take you to their main webpage, and you've got to dig around for the Medicare Supplement link. There are no ratings, no specific prices listed, and no ability to apply for Medicare Supplement plans through Medicare.gov—just links to insurance company websites, which, quite frankly, you can Google. Buying a Medicare Supplement plan through Medicare.gov can be very frustrating.

Having said all of the above, Medicare.gov is good for a few things. First of all, it's good if all you're trying to do is buy a stand-alone Medicare Part D Prescription Drug Plan to complement Original Medicare A and B with or without a Medicare Supplement. Later on in the book, I recommend you buy your Medicare Part D Prescription Drug Plan from Medicare.gov above all other options due to its ease and comprehensiveness.

Second of all, while it's not a great place to buy a Medicare Advantage plan, it is a great place to at least research all of the Medicare Advantage options available in your area.

Lastly, it hosts an absolute wealth of information about the Medicare program in general, from forms to re-ordering lost Medicare cards, the *Medicare and You* and related information guides, and more. There's a live chat section, you can register and create a Medicare.gov profile, and even file a complaint.

When you're ready to learn about the three Medicare plan coverage options, turn the page!

CHAPTER FOUR

# THE THREE MEDICARE PLAN COVERAGE OPTIONS

Now that you have a good overview of what Medicare is, some of its costs, benefits, and flaws, let's dive into the ways you can "consume" or use your Medicare benefits. There are generally three Medicare plan coverage paths to choose from.

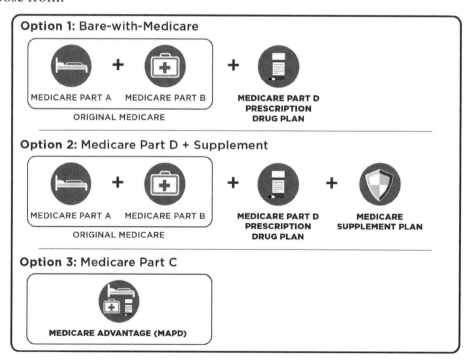

The information in this section is what many authors, journalists, insurance agents, and websites get wrong or don't fully cover. They usually only show you Options 2 and 3 and leave out Option 1. Is that because the commissions generated for insurance agencies and insurance agents made by the sales of Options 2 and 3 are so much higher than Option 1? Is that because Medicare insurance companies make way more money selling you products in Options 2 and 3? Or is it simply because Option 3 is actually better than going Bare-with-Medicare and cheaper than Option 2?

There's no clear answer, and it's likely a combination of all of them. In my experience, it's also because no insurance professional believes Option 1 is the best for anyone due to Frustrating Flaws one through three, which, again, are:

**1** No MOOP (Annual/Maximum Out Of Pocket)

**2** Medicare excess charges

**3** Coverage limitations

Using Medicare data, the latest of which displays information from 2016, researchers found that 19% of all people on Medicare had Option 1, and 29% of the Medicare population used Option 2. Using 2020 data, they found 36% used Option 3, and 30% had employer-based Medicare insurance coverage. I cover employer-based Medicare coverage in Chapter Eleven (Sources: PrepareforMedicare.com/sources).

These are the latest numbers I could find. If you do the math, they add up to 114%, which, of course, is impossible. Here's what I think has happened between 2016 and 2021.

Option 3, Medicare Advantage, continues to explode in popularity, jumping 7% since 2016. That leaves us 7% remaining and is probably explained by reduced or eliminated employer-sponsored coverage that has moved to Options 2 or 3 since then. Additionally, I'd also make an educated guess that we've seen a slight increase in Medicare Part D Prescription Drug + Medicare Supplement plan (Option 2) at the expense of Option 1, Original Medicare +

Medicare Part D Prescription Drug Plan during that time. I'd bet when there's a data refresh, we'll find that fewer than 19% of folks on Medicare now utilize Option 1, Bare-with-Medicare, Original Medicare Parts A and B plus a Part D Prescription Drug Plan.

**Which plan is right for you? It all depends on what you want. There's no one right choice. There could be multiple *best* options for you, but you've got to pick a path. For now, let's go over the three ways you can handle your Medicare.**

## THE THREE WAYS TO CONSUME YOUR MEDICARE BENEFITS

### OPTION 1: BARE-WITH-MEDICARE

This option is usually either glossed over by most authors, insurance agents, and pundits, or as I've discovered, left out completely as a solution. It seems as if everyone is talking about Medicare Advantage these days. Yet only 15-19% of the sixty-seven million people on Medicare use this option. Why? My guess is that most would argue it doesn't make sense to not fill in the gaps in financial coverage Original Medicare has, especially when there are insurance products (Medicare Advantage and Medicare Supplements) that will. Perhaps it's because insurance agents make pretty nice commissions selling those products, while they don't make much at all if they only sell you a Medicare Part D Prescription Drug Plan. Another guess is because insurance companies spend millions of dollars per year advertising those products, people naturally assume you need one. No, not everyone has a Medicare Advantage or a Medicare Supplement plan, regardless of what your neighbors, your Medicare insurance agent, or the paid spokespeople on TV say.

If you're asking my opinion, it wouldn't be my first choice due to the Frustrating Flaws numbers 1-3 listed previously. Bare-with-Medicare means you don't have any network restrictions to deal with, and that's a big plus for most people. But it's an opinion—do with it what you will.

In this scenario, you use Original Medicare parts A and B for your medical insurance coverage and simply buy a Medicare Part D Prescription Drug Plan to cover your prescription drug insurance. That's it. Simple. You're done. Original Medicare handles the majority of your healthcare needs, and you're looking at buying a Medicare Part D Prescription Drug Plan from one of many Medicare insurance companies for your prescription drug needs. It works this way just fine. People have been using Original Medicare for their medical coverage since Harry and Bess. You'll have two cards in your wallet—your Original Medicare red, white, and blue card to use for medical needs, and a Medicare Part D Prescription Drug Plan card you'll use at your pharmacy. Expect to normally pay anywhere between $8-$60 per month for your Medicare Part D Prescription Drug Plan.

Unlike Original Medicare, which is administered by the federal government, Part D is administered and sold by insurance companies. There is no federal or public option. You can find a Medicare Part D Prescription Drug Plan through Medicare's website, but you buy it from an insurance company. You can also buy it straight from the insurance company's website, by calling them, or with the help of a Medicare insurance agent. I cover this later in the DIY section starting in Chapter Nine. If this is what you want to do, I recommend you simply use Medicare.gov to enroll in your Medicare Part D Prescription Drug Plan when you're able, and you're all set.

Using Original Medicare Parts A and B and buying a Medicare Part D Prescription Drug Plan is the most straightforward, easiest process that exists when it comes to consuming your Medicare benefits.

Yes, yes . . . I just wrote an entire section on the Frustrating Flaws of Medicare. I didn't forget that, and they still apply. But, if you're simply not worried about a MOOP or Medicare Excess Charges and don't care about the bells and whistles found in a Medicare Advantage plan, this option is fine. I wouldn't necessarily recommend it due to those Frustrating Flaws, but I get it if you're unconcerned. Not everyone thinks like me, and *millions* of people consume their Medicare this way and are absolutely fine with it.

## OPTION 1: HOW MEDICARE INSURANCE COMPANIES MAKE MONEY

At this point, some of you may be wondering how insurance companies get paid for offering Medicare Part D Prescription Drug Plans. Certainly, they can't make ends meet by charging you $10 per month. Well, you're right; they can't. Remember when I said Medicare Part D insurance companies are essentially government contractors? That's because, in addition to your premium, the insurance companies get a subsidy per person, per month from Medicare. In my experience, profit margins on these plans are between 1-3% for insurance companies.

In 2021, Medicare's actuaries estimate that Medicare Part D plans receive direct subsidy payments averaging $216 per enrollee, per year. If the person is receiving a Low-Income Subsidy (LIS) to help them, that number goes to around $2,000 per year. This is in addition to the monthly premium amount they get from you, the consumer (Sources: PrepareforMedicare.com/sources).

Medicare Part D insurance companies also get additional funds for what's called risk-adjustment. That allows the insurance company to file for extra reimbursement from Medicare for very high-cost enrollees. That moves the annual amount to around $1,000 in payments for very high-cost enrollees (Sources: PrepareforMedicare.com/sources).

When you're buying or considering purchasing a Medicare Part D Prescription Drug Plan, there are a few key similarities each plan has, and they all vary by company. *These apply to Part D benefits embedded into Medicare Advantage plans, too.*

## FORMULARIES

Each Medicare insurance company offers a list of drugs they cover, and they list them on what's called a formulary. Medicare says the companies have to cover at least two drugs in every major drug category, but which specific drugs they offer are up to the plans. The price they charge and which tier they're under within the formulary is also up to the company. This is the main reason why you need to enter your drugs into Medicare.gov or the company's website while shopping for a Medicare Part D Prescription Drug Plan or a Medicare Advantage plan with Part D benefits embedded. If you're using an agent, it will be extremely helpful for both of you if you share the names of your prescription drugs with them so they can look them up and figure out which plan is best for you.

## TIERS

Within the formulary, prescription drugs will be categorized into tiers. These tiers are usually labeled 1-5, each with different copays or coinsurance amounts. Tier 1 drugs are usually the cheapest, Tier 5 the most expensive.

**Tier 1:** Preferred Generics

**Tier 2:** Non-preferred Generics

**Tier 3:** Preferred Brand Drugs

**Tier 4:** Non-preferred Brand Drugs

**Tier 5:** Specialty Drugs

Formulary tiers vary from plan to plan; sometimes, they come with six tiers. Soon, Medicare is expected to allow seven tiers.

## PRIOR AUTHORIZATION

Medicare insurance companies may require your doctors or other health providers to prove you need certain drugs before you can fill a prescription at the pharmacy. To do this, the insurance company could ask them to submit their medical reasoning, medical history, lab results, current symptoms, and treatment history. Most, if not all, Medicare Part D benefits have a Prior Authorization component, but the drug categories and individual drugs within the programs vary by company and the plan they're on. There are two types of reviews: Standard and Expedited. If you're having trouble getting approvals or need the review to happen quickly, you may want to specifically ask for an Expedited Review.

Prior Authorizations are typically found on brand-name prescription drugs that have a generic option available, drugs that have the potential to be abused, drugs used for cosmetic reasons, drugs that may have adverse health effects, or that are dangerous when combined with other medications.

## STEP THERAPY

Medicare insurance companies may require you to try a less expensive drug than the one prescribed by your doctor. For instance, let's say you were prescribed a made-up drug, MattsDrug. MattsDrug helps lower cholesterol, but it's brand new and costs $500. Let's also say there are plenty of cholesterol-lowering medications on the market that are cheaper alternative medications that do the same thing as MattsDrug.

Medicare rules say that the company must first give you a limited supply of MattsDrug because that's what your doctor prescribed. However, the company will have a problem with that because there are plenty of cheaper alternative medications out there that will do the same thing for less money. So, the insurance company will make you, or attempt to make you, switch to a less expensive drug that's been shown to be effective in lowering cholesterol. If that doesn't work, they'll try and make you take another drug, slightly more expensive than the first alternative but still cheaper than MattsDrug. If that doesn't work, *then* you can get MattsDrug.

To get MattsDrug without all of this hassle, your prescribing doctor will have to file what's called an Exception. This is just what it sounds like; the doctor will have to ask the Medicare insurance company to make an exception to their Step Therapy rules to get them to cover MattsDrug.

## QUANTITY LIMITS

Simply put, Medicare insurance companies place limits on the number of certain medications you can buy at one time. This is to protect against abuse and waste. There are also exceptions your doctor or health provider can ask for if you bump up against these and have good reasons for not being subject to them.

## MEDICARE PART D NETWORKS

Most Medicare Part D plans will come with a preferred network and a non-preferred network, although what they call them might be different. Get your prescriptions from preferred pharmacies and your costs will be lower. Get them from non-preferred pharmacies and they'll be higher. Essentially, insurance companies contract better pricing (for them and often, for you) with those preferred brick-and-mortar or mail-order pharmacies and do not get the same deals with non-preferred pharmacies.

## WHICH MEDICARE PART D PRESCRIPTION DRUG PLANS ARE "THE BEST?"

If by "best," you mean, "lowest premium," that's a pretty easy answer. Just use Medicare.gov as I outline in the DIY section, which you'll find in Chapter Nine. This answer changes almost every year, however, and I don't recommend prioritizing your Medicare Part D purchasing decisions solely based on the monthly premium. That is unless of course, you don't take any prescriptions and you're just buying a Medicare Part D Prescription Drug Plan so you don't get the Part D late enrollment penalty. In that case, I'd recommend you make sure your preferred pharmacy location is in the plan's network and *then* go with the lowest premium.

If by "best," you mean, it covers all of your prescriptions, then you're going to have to do the research on Medicare.gov, which I also outline how to do in Chapter Nine.

If by "best," you mean, no deductibles, lowest copays, and all of your prescriptions are covered, that too is going to take a bit of research on Medicare.gov.

If by "best," you mean, the most consistent, predictable benefits and monthly premiums, then my advice would be to stick with plans that have been available in your area for quite some time. You want to make sure the Medicare Part D Prescription Drug Plan you're on or are considering is stable. This generally means they have a large number (in the millions) of customers, and it's a brand you know and trust.

## OPTION 1: PROS AND CONS

Simple. Lower premiums than Option #2. Easy to DIY. Likely the lowest cost for hospitalization when compared to Option 3, Medicare Advantage. No networks for medical coverage.

No MOOP, so financial exposure is technically unlimited. Twenty percent coinsurance for medical. Potential exposure to Medicare excess charges. Limited overseas travel coverage. Doesn't offer "extra" coverage that Medicare Advantage plans can offer. Deductibles and premiums go up every year. Preferred vs. non-preferred pharmacies might surprise you with higher costs.

★ ★ ★ ★ ★

If you'd like to get an idea of the Medicare Part D insurance landscape, I've included interesting links on the website and a graphic outlining the largest insurance companies by customers.

## OPTION 2: MEDICARE PART D + SUPPLEMENT

Under this scenario, you buy a Medicare Part D Prescription Drug Plan outlined in the prior section to cover your prescription drugs, keep Original Medicare, and also buy a Medicare Supplement plan to insure yourself for the portion of medical costs Original Medicare doesn't cover. Approximately 29% of the sixty-seven million people on Medicare use this option.

Medicare Supplement plans available for purchase today do *not* cover Medicare Part D prescription drugs, so if you go this route, you will have to buy two insurance policies—a Medicare Supplement policy from company 1, and a Medicare Part D Prescription Drug Plan from company 2. This also means you'll have to pay for two separate insurance policies. Sometimes company 1 and company 2 can be the same company—there's no harm in that. But, generally, these two types of insurance plans *don't coordinate*. In other words, they don't talk to each other, so there's no real advantage of bundling both together. This means you'll have three insurance cards in your wallet, your Original Medicare card, one for the Medicare Supplement plan you use for your medical needs and a Medicare Part D Prescription Drug Plan card you'll use at the pharmacy for your prescription drugs.

## MEDICARE SUPPLEMENTS

In order to buy a Medicare Supplement plan, you *must* have Original Medicare Parts A and B.

Before the meteoric rise of Medicare Advantage plans beginning in 2006-2007, this was really the only option you had to fill in the gaps of Original Medicare, like the MOOP issue and the Excess Charges issue from the first two Frustrating Flaws of Medicare. That's why sometimes Medicare Supplements are also called Medigap plans. Different people will call them either one of those, usually depending on what part of the country you live in.

Medicare Supplement plans have been around for a very long time but came under federal oversight in the early 1980s and have undergone several transformations since then. Today, Medicare Supplement plans come in several flavors, which have letters attached to them. These are A, B, C, D, F, High-F, G, High-G, K, L, M, and N. There's also something called Medicare Select Plans, which are essentially Medicare Supplement plans with networks. I wouldn't pay much attention to those because they're pretty scarce, come with network restrictions, and not many folks buy them.

If you happen to live in Massachusetts, Minnesota, or Wisconsin, you may have options to choose from in addition to the letters I listed above. Also, you can't buy Medicare Supplement plans F, High-F, or C if you became eligible for Medicare after January 1, 2020. If you already have one, you can keep it (and I probably would).

Yes, it's a bit confusing to name Medicare Supplement plans with letters that also happen to be some of the same letters associated with Original Medicare Parts A and B, Medicare Part D, or Medicare Part C (Medicare Advantage). Why did they do this? I have no idea. Just know the letters associated with Medicare Supplement plans do not correlate at all to Original Medicare's A, B, C, and D. You can head over to the website for a nice chart of all of the different types of Medicare Supplement plans. However, I only recommend you pay attention to Plans G and N, as they offer the most comprehensive coverage. If you turned sixty-five prior to January 1, 2020, then I'd pay attention to C and F as well.

Medicare Supplements F and G are the only two that cover Frustrating Flaw #2 – Medicare Part B Excess Charges.

You can find the chart that outlines what all the letters or flavors of Medicare Supplement plans do at the website PrepareforMedicare.com/links.

**Medicare Supplements are *not* Medicare Advantage plans. They don't have anything to do with the notion of Managed Care, which is defined by Oxford Languages as "a system of healthcare in which patients agree to visit only certain doctors and hospitals, and in which the cost of treatment is monitored by a managing company." They are simply insurance policies that fill in the gaps of Medicare after Medicare has paid their portion.**

There are no HMO or PPO networks to mess with (except for the rare Select plans). There aren't teams of people in place at the insurance company to make sure you're getting the proper care if, say, you're a diabetic or have a heart condition. If your doctor says you need an MRI, there are no Medicare insurance company rules. There are actually very few Medicare rules that make your doctor jump through hoops to get Medicare to pay for most procedures. (Sources: PrepareforMedicare.com/sources.) There are typically no bells and whistles or extra benefits like dental coverage, meals, or transportation services embedded in these policies. The policies are simply paying what's billed after Medicare pays out its portion.

Here's how they work. Medicare Supplement plans have to be licensed and are regulated by the state and federal government, but unlike Medicare Advantage and Medicare Part D Prescription Drug Plans, the states really take the lead here. That's why there are so many state-based exceptions to the plans offered and the renewal timeframes. In fact, when you have a complaint about a Medicare Supplement insurance company, you don't usually call Medicare; most of the time, you call the state Department of Insurance to complain. Each year, insurance companies must meet a long list of requirements from each state to continue to offer the plans and, when necessary, change their premiums. Sometimes, the states reject a company's plans for increasing premiums. (I've seen it happen!)

## OPTION 2: HOW MEDICARE SUPPLEMENT INSURANCE COMPANIES MAKE MONEY

Since Medicare Supplement policies don't receive any federal Medicare subsidies or risk adjustment payments, they only get money to pay claims for their customers from the monthly premiums they charge. That's why premiums for Medicare Supplement plans are typically in the $120-$280 per month range, while premiums for Medicare Advantage are much lower. According to my friends in the Medicare Supplement insurance companies, profit margins are slim here as well, usually ranging between 1-4%.

## WHICH MEDICARE SUPPLEMENT IS "THE BEST?"

Well, it depends on your definition. If by "best," you mean, provides the most comprehensive coverage, then I'd say Plan G because, after you pay your annual Medicare Part B deductible, it pays for everything else, and it will also pay for any Medicare Excess Charges you may run into. Coming in a close second to Plan G would be Plan N. The big difference between Plan G and Plan N is that Plan G covers Medicare Part B Excess Charges while Plan N does not. (Prior to 2020, my answer would have been Plan F which covers that

Part B deductible plus any potential Medicare Excess charges.)

With Plan N, you'll have to pay copays of up to $20 for some office visits, or up to $50 if you go to the emergency room but aren't admitted. Plan G covers both of these at 100%.

If by "best," you mean cheapest, then I'd say High-G. This is a Plan G with a High Deductible. In 2021, that deductible was $2,370, and you would have paid that before any benefits kicked in. These premiums can be as cheap as $30 per month.

Original Medicare + Medicare Part D Prescription Drug + Medicare Supplement plan is really almost a set-it-and-forget-it way of consuming your Medicare benefits. The Medicare Supplement plans are straightforward—they pay after Original Medicare, and you never (rarely) need to worry about filing claims paperwork. If you buy a Plan G this year, those benefits don't change . . . ever. If you like the Medicare Supplement plan you're on, as long as you keep paying the premiums, nothing changes. You don't have to worry about using insurance company networks. Yes, you have to buy a Medicare Part D Prescription Drug Plan from an insurance company, and you've got Medicare Housekeeping to do every October 1 (covered in Chapter Ten) to make sure that Medicare Part D Prescription Drug Plan still meets your needs. But if you can navigate a website, that's pretty easy for you to do yourself.

## OPTION 2: PROS AND CONS

 SIMPLICITY - STANDARDIZED PLANS

All insurance companies offering Medicare Supplement coverage use the same letters. Each letter has a standard benefit, and they don't vary from company to company. This means, if you buy a Medicare Supplement plan G from United Healthcare, it's the same as buying a Medicare Supplement plan G from Mutual of Omaha or any other company. The medical benefits are exactly the same except for the price. It pays to shop for the best price.

## GUARANTEED RENEWABILITY

As long as you keep paying your monthly premium, the insurance company can't kick you off the plan, even if you get deathly ill. If, for some reason, they go out of business, Medicare will let you switch to another plan in your area, no problem. The only person who can cancel your policy is you as long as you keep paying your premiums.

## BENEFITS DO NOT CHANGE

Unlike Medicare Advantage and Medicare Part D Prescription Drug Plans, the benefits do not change every year. If you buy a Medicare Supplement plan G, it will *always* provide the same level and amount of coverage after you pay your Part B deductible.

## NETWORKS? NOPE.

Remember, in this scenario, you're actually still on Original Medicare, just buying a Medicare Supplement to layer on top of that. Any doctor, facility, or hospital that accepts Medicare assignment will take a Medicare Supplement anywhere in the country. That's because first, they're billing Medicare Parts A and B, and anything left over they'll send to the Medicare Supplement insurance company to pay. Medicare Supplements offer the most provider choice, period. You don't have to make sure anyone is in-network before you go. You just . . . go.

As we've seen, it's pretty darn hard to find a doctor or hospital that won't accept Medicare assignment. Odds are extremely high that whomever you go to, they'll accept Original Medicare patients, which means Medicare Supplement patients. When you have a Medicare Advantage plan, you have a network of doctors to go to, and doctors and hospitals drop in and out of these networks all the time.

## NO PROVIDER NETWORK HOOPS TO JUMP THROUGH

Concerned about getting permission, Prior Authorizations, or the insurance company generally making your doctor jump through hoops to get something approved and paid? If your doctor thinks you need an MRI, he or she orders an MRI, and you get an MRI. Those annoying hoops generally don't exist in Medicare Supplement-land. If Original Medicare says it's covered, then the Medicare Supplement insurance companies simply pay what's left over. There are rarely any questions. In fact, my friends in the insurance industry have told me the claims auto-adjudication rate is above 90%. This means computers process over 90% of Medicare supplement claims sent in by providers and approve them. **Another way to look at it is that 90% of the time, a human never has to decide whether or not to pay your claim, which makes this interaction very easy. If Original Medicare pays your claim, your Medicare Supplement plan usually pays. Period.**

## 👍 NO REFERRALS REQUIRED

Unlike some Medicare Advantage plans (HMO plans, generally), you don't have to go to your primary care physician first before you get permission or a referral to see a specialist. Does your foot hurt? Go right to a podiatrist. Knee pain? Go right to an orthopedic specialist.

## 👍 TRAVEL

As I mentioned above, within the USA and its territories, there are no network restrictions. That means, if you live in Missouri and spend a lot of time with family in Illinois, you can go to doctors in either state, and the coverage will be the exact same. You don't even have to check with the insurance company.

If you have Medicare Supplement plan C, D, F, G, M, or N, you even have some emergency coverage for overseas travel. However, it's limited to a $50,000-lifetime amount, and once you've been out of the US longer than sixty days, you're no longer covered by your Medicare supplement. There's also a $250 yearly deductible that you must meet before your plan kicks in, and then you'll have coinsurance to pay after the deductible up to a certain dollar amount, commonly $50,000. Just like in the US, your Medicare Supplement plan will only pay if the claims would normally be Medicare-approved. However, Original Medicare (Bare-with-Medicare) actually pays nothing for foreign travel.

Before you leave, call your Medicare Supplement company to give them a heads-up before you depart. If you do have medical services overseas, you'll have to file your own claims with your Medicare Supplement insurance company to get reimbursed. That's not fun, but if you're really worried, remember; you can always buy extra insurance when you go overseas.

## PREDICTABLE SPENDING

While the monthly insurance premiums for Medicare Supplements are certainly higher than those of Medicare Advantage, the difference is in coverage. When you buy a Medicare Supplement plan G and pay your Part B deductible, you're done. You won't pay out of pocket for anything else that's Original Medicare-approved for the rest of the calendar year. Not true for Medicare Advantage plans, which have a dizzying array of deductibles, coinsurances, and copays.

## NO ANNUAL REVIEW

Because Medicare Supplement plans are standardized, the benefits never change. Ever. If you buy a Plan G today, those benefits will be the same for the rest of your life. Thus, you don't have to do an annual review or worry about what's changing in your Medicare Supplement plan every year, like you do with Medicare Advantage. Medicare Supplements are as close as you can get to set-it-and-forget-it Medicare coverage.

## LESS PAPERWORK, LESS HASSLE

If Original Medicare pays your medical claim, your Medicare Supplement plan works with your medical provider's billing office to send payment right to them, bypassing the need for you to get involved. Plan payments are straightforward; if Original Medicare paid, the Medicare Supplement insurance company pays what it should. Period.

## MOVE TO A MEDICARE ADVANTAGE PLAN ANYTIME

You don't need to keep your Option 2: Medicare Part D Prescription Drug Plan + Medicare Supplement plan if it gets too expensive or you just don't like it. You can move to a Medicare Advantage plan during any AEP (October 15-December 7 every year). But remember, be careful if you decide to do this. (See Chapter Two for more on election periods.)

## DISCOUNT PROGRAMS AND SPECIAL BENEFITS

Some Medicare Supplement insurance companies offer premium discounts for spouses and partners buying together, gym memberships, and other items.

## PREMIUMS

Medicare Supplements aren't cheap. A Medicare Supplement plan G can easily cost you $150 per month when you're under seventy, and well over $200 when you're over seventy.

## NO PRESCRIPTION DRUG COVERAGE

Don't forget, Medicare Supplement plans don't cover outpatient prescription drugs, so you'll have to buy a Medicare Part D Prescription Drug Plan, too. Those can cost anywhere between $8-$60 on top of the Medicare Supplement premium.

## RISING PREMIUM PRICES AS YOU GET OLDER

If you have a Medicare Advantage plan, the monthly premium price is the price, regardless of age; the monthly premium is the same for everybody. Not so with Medicare Supplements—the price can go up the older you get. However, what Medicare Supplement companies cannot do is charge you more if you get sick, and less if you do not.

Medicare Supplement prices are often different for men and women; they're usually priced higher for men. Medicare Supplements often provide discounts for signing up at age sixty-five, or for signing up a spouse or partner at the same time (called household discounts) but cost more if you use tobacco. Some of those discounts go away after age sixty-five.

**It's important to note (again) premiums usually go up every year, and some companies offer discounts for the first year. Don't get fooled by sixty-five-year-old pricing.**

Hit the website for a link to see a summary of prices in major metropolitan areas. PrepareforMedicare.com/links.

There are three types of pricing methodologies that Medicare Supplements can have, usually listed from least to most expensive.

1. Attained-Age—the most common pricing methodology. The older you get, the more it costs. Again, don't be fooled by introductory pricing. Take a look in the pamphlet or online at what it will cost every year. It's there; you just might have to search for it.

2. Issue-Age—whatever the monthly premium is when you sign up, will be what it is until you cancel it.

3. Community Pricing—the monthly premiums stay the same regardless of your age. It won't go up just because you get older.

Medicare Supplement plan monthly premiums usually have rate increases every year, and not always centered around the beginning or the end of the year. Often, it's on your policy anniversary, which may not line up with Medicare's AEP for Medicare Advantage and the Medicare Part D Prescription Drug Plan you have.

## MEDICAL UNDERWRITING

If you're turning sixty-five or getting Medicare for the first time, it's extremely important to know there are only certain times you can buy a Medicare Supplement without being asked health questions. If you buy a Medicare Supplement within the first six months of getting Medicare Part B, the insurance company has to accept you. *This is called the one-time Medicare Supplement (Medigap) Open Enrollment Period.* **If you don't sign up for a Medicare Supplement plan within this timeframe, you will**

**probably have to answer health questions and could be denied coverage. If you've previously been or are very sick (cancer, heart attack, stroke, etc.) before you got Medicare and want to make sure you can get a Medicare Supplement plan with no health questions, *it is paramount you don't miss this window.***

Several states have exceptions to this. In California, you can switch your Medicare Supplement plans between carriers (as long as it's not an upgrade) every year in the sixty days following your birthday with no medical underwriting. In Oregon, you have thirty days. In Missouri, you can switch within sixty days of your anniversary date of your initial effective date into a Medicare Supplement plan. Washington, New York, Connecticut, Minnesota, and Wisconsin also have special rules that may allow you to switch. If you're in any of these states, I highly suggest you talk to a representative from a Medicare Supplement insurance company or a Medicare insurance agent to help guide you through the process. Planning ahead is key here—don't wait until the last minute or drop your current coverage without doing your homework or getting help.

##  MEDICARE SUPPLEMENT GUARANTEE ISSUE RIGHTS

There are other scenarios where people may be able to get Medicare Supplement insurance outside of the Medicare Supplement (Medigap) Open Enrollment Period. Some rules are federal, some are state-based. If this applies to you, your best bet is to lean on an expert Medicare insurance agent for guidance. Independent Medicare insurance agents in your area know the state-based rules, as do telephone representatives working for Medicare Supplement insurance companies. Medicare.gov has a nice webpage outlining these scenarios and you can find the link to that page by going to PrepareforMedicare.com/links.

## LOOKBACK PERIODS

Depending on when you sign up, the insurance company might not treat a pre-existing condition for the first six months. Original Medicare will cover its portion, but the Medicare Supplement insurance plan may not cover the rest.

Again, if you think this might apply to you, I'd talk to a representative from a Medicare Supplement insurance company or a Medicare insurance agent to help guide you through the process.

## SWITCHING BETWEEN MEDICARE ADVANTAGE AND MEDICARE SUPPLEMENT

Want to drop your Medicare Part D Prescription Drug + Medicare Supplement plan and go to an all-in-one Medicare Advantage plan during the AEP between October 15 and December 7 of each year? No problem! Want to switch back later? Potentially a *big* problem! You can do this *only once*, and you can only do this within twelve months of such a switch, and you'll have to use a Special Enrollment exception to do it. This is called your "Trial Right" period. If you miss the window, you'll most likely be asked health questions and possibly be denied coverage if you want to re-sign up for a Medicare Supplement plan. Several states may have their own special rules. Again, I'd recommend not doing this until you talk to a representative from a Medicare Supplement insurance company or a Medicare insurance agent to help guide you through the process. Plan ahead—don't wait until the AEP starts and decide you want to do this. If you do this, you must call and cancel your Medicare Supplement yourself; the Medicare Advantage company won't do it for you.

It's tempting to think you can enroll in a Medicare Advantage plan when you're sixty-five and keep it for a few years *then* switch to a Medicare Supplement when you get sick and start to rack up medical bills. Of course, everyone wants the most comprehensive medical insurance coverage when they're sick, but it doesn't work that way. That's why you need to not only think about today but also *tomorrow*. **If you want to buy a Medicare Supplement when you're already sick, odds are, you'll be denied coverage.** The only exceptions to this are:

**1** If you sign up for a Medicare Advantage plan at sixty-five and want to switch to a Medicare Supplement plan within the first twelve months. You can do this using your "Trial Right" Special Election Period, but it has to be within the first twelve months of having that Medicare Advantage plan.

**2** If you had a Medicare Supplement plan, *then* switched to a Medicare Advantage plan and want to switch *back* to a Medicare Supplement plan. You can also do this using your "Trial Right" Special Election Period, but it has to be within the first twelve months of having that Medicare Advantage plan.

**3** State-specific Guarantee Issue rules and certain Guarantee Issue Medicare Supplement plans.

## NO BELLS AND WHISTLES

Think you might want all the *cool stuff* like transportation to doctor's appointments, grocery delivery, over-the-counter allowances, gym memberships, fitness classes, or dental, vision, or hearing insurance included? Nope, not usually. That "cool stuff" can only be embedded into Medicare Advantage plans.

If you'd like to get an idea of the Medicare Supplement insurance landscape, there are some items on PrepareforMedicare.com/links.

From my viewpoint, the largest Medicare Supplement insurance companies, ranked from the most to least customers, are brands you already know. The order of this list is an educated guess, as I can't find an official list anywhere online that's a reliable, reputable source. I'm pretty confident my rankings aren't that far off, however.

**1** Blue Cross and Blue Shield

**2** United Healthcare (co-branded with AARP)

**3** Mutual of Omaha

**4** CVS Health/Aetna

**5** Cigna

**6** Humana

## OPTION 3: MEDICARE PART C

**MEDICARE ADVANTAGE (MAPD)**

In this scenario, you buy a Medicare Advantage plan that covers your medical costs as well as your Medicare Part D prescription drug coverage. Remember, these are Medicare Part C plans. These are combo plans—they cover the medical benefits of Original Medicare Parts A and B, as well as D. Approximately 35% of the sixty-seven million people on Medicare use this option. At a glance, it's easy to see why. Premiums for these range from $0 to over $100, but most people pay $0 to about $40 per month for these. It's a pretty compelling package to consider—you get Medicare Parts A, B, and D all in one package for a relatively low (or no) premium, hence its popularity.

These plans look sort of like traditional insurance you get from work, except, in most cases, they are far better. There are low copays for doctor visits, deductibles, coinsurance, and all of them *must* have a MOOP (eliminating Original Medicare Frustrating Flaw #1). Oftentimes, they do not have a deductible or coinsurances for many services. When they do, it's usually for using doctors who are not in their provider network, or for certain categories of prescription drugs.

Many Medicare Advantage plans offer additional benefits that Original Medicare does not. Examples of this are dental, vision, and hearing coverage, post-discharge meals, and gym memberships.

Recall from earlier in the book that you cannot buy a federal or public-option Medicare Advantage plan. Medicare Advantage comes in a few shapes and sizes, but the vast majority of them are technically called Medicare

Advantage-Prescription Drug plans. You might remember this acronym, pronounced M-A-P-D. There are MA-only plans out there, but those aren't the ones we're talking about here. Those are generally for veterans and folks on TRICARE. (I cover this towards the end of the book in Chapter Ten.)

When you buy one of these, it means, unlike the prior options, you don't flash your red, white, and blue Original Medicare card when you go to the doctor's office—you put it in your top drawer. Do *not* throw it away, but it won't work anymore. You get one card from the insurance company to use at the medical provider's office, the hospital, and at the pharmacy.

In order to buy a Medicare Advantage plan, you *must* have Original Medicare Parts A and B. You cannot simultaneously have a Medicare Supplement and a Medicare Advantage, nor can you simultaneously have a stand-alone Medicare Part D Prescription Drug Plan and an MAPD plan. Again, any combination of Option 1 or Option 2 from above will not work with an MAPD plan. To put it another way, you can have either Option 1 *or* Option 2, but *neither of them* if you choose Option 3, Medicare Advantage.

Remember, that's because an MAPD plan is an all-in-one combo plan. If you enroll in a stand-alone Medicare Part D Prescription Drug Plan while you already have an MAPD plan, you'll get kicked off the MAPD plan. At the same time, if you already have a Medicare Part D Prescription Drug Plan and sign up for an MAPD plan, you'll automatically get kicked off the Part D plan. Tread carefully.

The average cost for an MAPD is $29, according to the Kaiser Family Foundation, but many people are on $0 premium plans. Yes, $0 premium. People in the Medicare insurance industry aren't allowed to say they're free because they're not. They're just $0 per month. I know it sounds silly, but the reason is that it's not technically free because you earned your Medicare benefits by paying into the system for all of those years.

Using Medicare Advantage plans to cover your prescription drug and medical costs isn't a set-it-and-forget-it way to consume your Medicare. It's tricky and complex to buy, the premiums and benefits can (and do!) change every year, and insurance companies make you use their HMO or PPO networks. If you go this route, there are certainly benefits to doing so, and a third of the entire Medicare population can't all be wrong—you'll have to do some Medicare Housekeeping (Chapter Ten) every year to make sure the plan you have *this* year is the best plan for you *next* year.

## A BRIEF HISTORY OF MEDICARE ADVANTAGE

Back in 2003, President George W. Bush signed the Medicare Modernization Act. In addition to introducing prescription drug coverage for the Medicare population, the government outlined and enhanced financial incentives for insurance companies to bring managed care into the Medicare arena to bring down how much Medicare costs the federal government and, of course, in the end, how much it costs you, the taxpayer. Remember that managed care is loosely described as a system of healthcare in which patients agree to visit only certain doctors and hospitals, and in which the cost of treatment is monitored by a managing company. In a nutshell, you can think of it as ensuring appropriate health management and cost controls are in place for Medicare recipients. Prior to that, Original Medicare was, and still is today, what's called fee-for-service, which essentially means that when a medical provider bills them, Medicare pays with very few questions asked.

Has the introduction of managed care through out-sourcing Medicare to insurance companies worked? That depends on who you ask. In 2019, the Medicare Payment Advisory Commission estimated that Medicare payments to Medicare Advantage plans are roughly the same per person compared to people on Original Medicare. So, by that measure, maybe not. An article by the *New York Times* in 2017 suggested Medicare Advantage actually costs the government *more* money than Original Medicare, with several caveats. (Sources: PrepareforMedicare.com/sources). Yet, other studies purport that's not the case, and it actually does lower overall Medicare costs for people. The jury is out and the debate continues.

Whether or not Medicare Advantage plans are technically cheaper for the American taxpayer on a per-person basis is up for debate. But there's no debate when it comes to coverage. There's very little question that Medicare Advantage plans can offer much better overall benefit options and provide much more financial protection when compared to Original Medicare. The American people seem to agree, as they've become extremely popular, particularly in the last decade. Today, more than a third of all people on Medicare have a Medicare Advantage plan.

Here's how they work. Medicare insurance companies file bids once a year for the ability to provide these plans to the general public. There are hundreds of rules to follow, and in my experience, the annual bid process begins at most companies in January the prior year and they're all wrapped up by late May and early June. I've been very involved in this annual bid process over the course of my career, and I can tell you it's a grueling five-month-long process. This stuff is complicated. Because companies are playing the part of Medicare sub-contractor, that means Medicare makes all the rules. One of the rules is Medicare Advantage plans must cover everything Original Medicare Parts A and B cover, at a minimum. Beyond the minimum, insurance companies can make their benefits better than those found in Original Medicare, which they do. They do this because there are a lot of insurance companies competing in this space and, of course, the insurance companies want to make a product that's attractive enough for someone to buy over their competitors' product.

Of course, businesses are in the business of, well, business, and they design their bids to include a percentage of profit. In my experience, that profit margin is between 1-4%. That means, *after* they pay all of the medical and prescription drug bills, their employees, and overhead, they make a very small, single-digit profit. Think insurance companies make money hand-over-fist on this stuff? Actually, their profit margins are much slimmer than you might have expected. The government *will* let companies bid at zero profit or even at a loss. Why would a company do that? To gain market share. But I digress.

When the Medicare insurance company is approved to offer a Medicare Advantage plan, they can begin to sell their product. Medicare Advantage contracts are only good for one year, and they must be rebid and be renewed every year. That's why the benefits and monthly premiums *only* stay the same for a calendar year—companies can adjust them annually, unlike Medicare Supplements which stay the same year over year. This is also why I urge you (in Chapter Ten) to re-shop your Medicare Advantage plan every year because things change every year. And they do change, sometimes for better, sometimes for worse.

## OPTION 3: HOW MEDICARE INSURANCE COMPANIES MAKE MONEY

Once the Medicare insurance company gets a customer, here's what happens, and it's really pretty simple. If you sign up for a Medicare Advantage plan, The Centers for Medicare and Medicaid (CMS) essentially turn all financial responsibility for paying claims over to the insurance company. Medicare is now off the hook to pay claims, and the insurance company is on the hook. In return, the insurance company gets a payment from Medicare every month. This is called a CAP rate, and these payments can run anywhere between $350 (American Samoa) and $1,700 (Nome, AK) (Sources: PrepareforMedicare.com/sources). These vary depending upon where you live and how much Medicare calculates healthcare costs in your area. The CAP rates are different for every county in America, which is also why Medicare Advantage plans are offered on a county-by-county basis. It's an over-simplification to say it's an average of these healthcare costs, but it's close enough to say it blends the costs of people in counties from the very healthy, who don't use any Original Medicare, to the very sick, who use millions of dollars' worth.

There's also something called risk adjustment, which we talked briefly about in the Medicare Part D section, that applies to Medicare Advantage plans, too. If someone is very sick or has a chronic condition, the insurance company can figure that out from billing codes and request more money from Medicare to help offset the increased costs those folks incur.

Ever wonder why Medicare Advantage companies really try hard to get you to see your doctors? Why your primary physician copays are so cheap at $0, $5, or only $10 to see your doctor, who clearly normally charges more than that? Why they might actually call you to urge you to go get a checkup? It's almost as if a car insurance company wanted you to get in a wreck so they can pay a claim. Seems counterintuitive, right? Well, it's not.

Insurance companies need a code indicating a diagnosis from your doctors so they can see if you have any of those chronic conditions or are very ill. Without those codes, they can't file for additional risk adjustment reimbursement from Medicare. If they don't get that additional reimbursement from Medicare, they lose money because they're not getting enough reimbursement to cover your healthcare costs. Even when they do, they often still lose money on people with chronic conditions or who are very sick.

If the insurance company has done a good job of this, and a good job of designing Medicare Advantage plans to attract not only the sick *but also the healthy people who don't spend as much* as the CAP rate they're getting from Medicare, it should all balance out so the insurance company can make a small profit. If they do a poor job at this, they lose money. That means the next time they go to bid, they probably make their benefits worse than the prior year (more expensive for you) and potentially increase their monthly premiums to make up for the loss. If things go really poorly for too long, they just cancel the Medicare Advantage plan, leaving you in a lurch and searching for a new plan for the following year. **They *can't* cancel you, but they *can* cancel the plan you're on. Yes, they're allowed to do that, and it happens all the time.** That's why I noted in Medicare Frustrating Flaw #4 that the Medicare.gov website doesn't display year-to-year changes to benefits if premiums go higher or lower every year for a particular product. If you're in a Medicare Advantage plan and the benefits keep getting worse while the premiums keep getting higher, that's a good indication that the plan isn't performing very well from a financial standpoint. As a Medicare consumer, I'd like to know which direction that plan is headed.

## WATCH YOUR MOOPS!

Frustrating Flaw #1 notes Original Medicare doesn't have a MOOP. Medicare Supplements take care of that flaw, as do Medicare Advantage plans. All Medicare Advantage plans, including those that charge nothing for the plan's premium, will have a MOOP. This means that once you have spent a certain amount of money each year on your Medicare services, you will not need to spend any more for your covered services that year. **The MOOP *only* applies to the medical component—the built-in prescription drug**

**benefits are on a separate schedule.** Also similar to other health insurance plans, the amount of this annual out-of-pocket maximum can vary a great deal from one Medicare Advantage plan to another. In 2021 and 2022, a Medicare Advantage plan may not have a MOOP that's higher than $7,550, but that's just a maximum number; many plans have a MOOP that's much lower than that. For PPO plans, the in-network MOOP limit is also set at a maximum of $7,550, but the out-of-network MOOP can be higher. On a PPO plan, no plan may charge an in-network and out-of-network MOOP that exceeds $11,300, combined.

## HOW ARE THE MONTHLY PREMIUMS SO LOW, AND SOMETIMES EVEN $0?

As you may have noticed, there are quite a few Medicare Advantage plans that you can get for a $0 monthly premium. How can this be? Well, let's go back to that CAP payment they get and the risk-adjustment process. Essentially, if you see a $0 MAPD plan, what that insurance company is saying is, *"we can take on your medical care and prescription drug needs, offer you a certain level of coverage with what we're getting from the feds, and not have to charge you any additional premium to make ends meet. At least, we think so. We hope so."* If they don't think they can cover the benefits and the costs with only the CAP rates they're getting from Medicare, then that's why a Medicare Advantage plan would charge you a monthly premium.

If you decide a Medicare Advantage plan is the way to go, this does not mean that your coverage will be free. Just like with other types of health insurance policies, Medicare Advantage plans have various deductibles, coinsurance, or copayment costs that you are responsible for. So, when you add those up over a typical year, in some instances, you may find your overall financial responsibility may even be more with a $0 premium plan than with an MAPD plan that charges a monthly premium.

## NETWORKS

Medicare Advantage plans come in three flavors. There are some minor exceptions but not enough to note here.

**1** **PPO–Preferred Provider Organization:** You can use any doctor and hospital in or out of the plan's network. Out-of-network providers do not have to accept you as a patient, nor is there a contractual obligation for them to bill your Medicare insurance company.

**2** **HMO–Health Maintenance Organization:** You cannot use any doctors out of the plan's network.

**3** **HMO–POS–Health Maintenance Organization–Point of Service:** While rare, these plans let you go out of the plan's network, often requiring a referral from a doctor who *is* in the network.

In order to control their costs (a key to managed care), Medicare insurance companies contract with a network of medical providers they either *force* you to use (HMO) or would *like* you to use (PPO). That's because the insurance company contracts with these medical providers who agree to charge certain prices in certain ways. If you stay in their networks, the prices you get charged are lower. This shouldn't be anything new to you; provider networks have been around since the first Blue Cross and Blue Shield plans were around in the 1930s, and you're probably very familiar with the concept if you ever had employer-sponsored health insurance or an ACA plan.

## NETWORK CHOICE

This phrase can mean many things to many people. Here, I'm using it to refer to the choice of doctors. It's simple; if you buy a Medicare Advantage plan, you're going to either be buying a version of an HMO or a PPO plan.

An HMO restricts your provider choices to those the insurance companies have contracted with, often in a geographic area or county. They may or may not have travel benefits if you go outside the network area. There are (usually) no out-of-network benefits. That is to say, if you go to a doctor or hospital outside of what's listed in your provider directory, the Medicare Advantage plan does not have to cover that expense.

For many people living in one area of the country, this works out just fine.

If they check and see that their doctor(s) are in the network and their preferred hospital or hospital system is as well, they're just fine staying in the network.

For others, a PPO might make more sense.

A PPO Medicare Advantage plan has, essentially, two networks. One is considered in-network, which is to say, the insurance company has a contract with these doctors and hospitals to bill preferential rates for their services. If you get care from the doctors and hospitals in the network, you pay less out of pocket.

However, the second network is everyone else who accepts Medicare and bills the insurance company. You can still go, but the amount of money you'll have to pay out-of-pocket can significantly increase. In other words, you have more choices, but you'll pay more for that choice if you choose to go outside of the network.

**I personally like PPO plans. I like having the option of going outside of my plan's network if I want or need to.** Would I pay a whole lot of premium to buy a PPO over an HMO? It all depends. How stark are the differences in benefits and cost? Ultimately, it's up to you. Some people hate the HMO acronym because they remember HMOs being dragged through the nightly news in the 1980s. For others, it works very well for them due to the managed care and great benefits.

## MEDICARE ADVANTAGE AVAILABILITY

Unlike Medicare Part D Prescription Drug Plans, which are filed by insurance companies based on regions, which often include multiple states, Medicare Advantage plans are filed and bid on a county-by-county basis. This means that, depending on where you live, you may have multiple Medicare Advantage plans in your area, or very few . . . or none.

Remember the example from the beginning of the book? Tim and Alex. Recall that Tim and Alex both live in Miami, which is in Miami-Dade County, home to one of the largest populations of people on Medicare. Tim and Alex have *forty-three* different Medicare Advantage plans available to them. It's a very competitive market with lots of Medicare insurance companies competing for Tim and Alex's business.

The same could be said for other large metropolitan areas with high populations of people on Medicare. As of 2021, in Phoenix (Maricopa County), there are fifty-two Medicare Advantage plans available. There are also fifty-two Medicare Advantage choices to choose from if you live in Chicago (Cook County) or Manhattan, NYC. You have fifty-five options if you live in Houston (Harris County) and forty-seven if you live in Seattle (King County).

However, if you live in Cape Girardeau, Missouri, you only have fourteen Medicare Advantage plans to choose from. In Missoula, Montana, you only have eleven options. In Cheyenne, Wyoming, you have zero.

As you can see from the examples above, it's a pretty fair statement to say that the larger the metropolitan area you live in, the more Medicare Advantage options you have available to purchase.

Why is this? Well, there are a bunch of reasons Medicare insurance companies choose to stay out of certain counties, but I'll cover a few of the more common ones below.

First on the list is the number of potential customers. Miami-Dade County has 430,000 people over the age of sixty-five living within its borders. Laramie County, Wyoming, has 14,800. It takes just as much effort for an insurance company to file a bid with Medicare in Miami-Dade as it does in Laramie County. Where would you go first? It's an easy answer—where the most potential customers reside.

Second on the list is provider access. It's no secret that there aren't enough doctors in rural areas, and rural hospitals are closing at an alarming rate. For a Medicare Advantage insurance company, this is often a barrier to expanding outside of metro areas. Medicare Advantage plans must establish networks of doctors and hospitals—PPO plans and HMO plans. In order to do that, they must prove to Medicare that they have enough doctors of every type—primary care physicians, psychiatrists, oncologists, etc., and hospitals included in their networks. This is called network adequacy, and if you don't meet what Medicare deems an adequate network, they'll deny your bid.

I remember working for an insurance company that was considering filing for a new county expansion in rural Arizona. We were asking doctors in Las

Vegas—over a two-hour drive away—to accept our patients. It wasn't because we wanted our potential customers to have to drive that far to see an in-network doctor; it was simply because that was the closest urologist in that part of the country that would contract with our insurance company!

That leads me to third on the list—competition. If you're the only hospital in town or within fifty miles, you can almost dictate the prices an insurance company needs to pay you for claims. It's all negotiable—there isn't a flat rate for every insurance company. If you're one of ten hospitals within fifty miles, well, then it gets more competitive for each hospital, and they're more willing to negotiate favorable rates with a particular or with multiple insurance companies. I've personally run into more than one situation where a doctor's group or hospital has held out for higher prices from the insurance company because they were the only game in town, and they knew it. The prices they were asking made it cost-prohibitive for the insurance company I was working for at the time, and we just decided not to open a plan in that county. I'm not faulting them—it's just a reality.

There are a whole host of other reasons why an insurance company would or would not file a Medicare Advantage plan in a certain area, much of it data driven. What does the publicly available healthcare quality data show? Is the quality of care provided by healthcare providers better or worse on average compared to their peers nationally? Does the population of the area have a higher rate of diabetes, congestive heart failure, or other chronic conditions? Or are they lower than other areas?

This is all to say, while you might like to buy a Medicare Advantage plan, you might not be able to, depending on where you live. Or, because there aren't enough insurance companies offering them, they may not be that great of a deal due to a lack of competition. If there are only two Medicare Advantage insurance companies offering plans in the area, they may not file plans with very rich benefits because they don't have to. If they're competing with fifteen other insurance companies for the same consumer, the competition is increased, and they fight harder with competitive premiums and benefits for the Medicare consumer.

## WHICH MEDICARE ADVANTAGE PLANS ARE "THE BEST?"

This is an impossible question to answer. Unlike Medicare Supplement plans, no two Medicare Advantage plans are alike. Premiums, benefits, add-on offerings, drug coverage—they all vary, not only by company but by plan. Those companies and plans vary by where you live and from year to year. Nationwide, 3,148 Medicare Advantage plans were available for individual enrollment for the 2020 plan year—an increase of 414 plans since 2019. The average person on Medicare was able to choose among twenty-eight plans in 2020, up from twenty-four in 2019. (Sources: PrepareforMedicare.com/sources).

If by "best," you mean, "provider choice," then I'd say you're going to want to look at a Medicare Advantage PPO plan. These plans have networks of preferred doctors, hospitals, and other Medicare health providers, but you can go outside of their networks, too. It'll just cost you more money when you do.

If by "best," you mean, "lowest cost," that's a pretty tough question to answer, too. Generally, Medicare Advantage HMO plans offer the lowest premiums, best benefits, and lowest MOOPs. But that's not always the case, and many PPO plans have recently been priced with $0 premiums.

**I'd also watch out for Medicare Advantage plans with deductibles.** More and more insurance companies are introducing those on their medical benefits *and* their prescription drug benefits as a way to keep their monthly premiums lower. This means that before any of your plan benefits kick in, you must first pay a deductible for either your medical coverage or your prescription drug coverage—and in some instances, both!

If by "best," you mean, the most consistent, predictable benefits and monthly premiums, then my advice would be to stick with plans that have been available in your area for quite some time. You want to make sure the Medicare Advantage plan you're on or are considering is stable.

## MEDICARE ADVANTAGE PLAN STABILITY

Since Medicare Supplements have been around for decades and have standardized plans, there are usually very few instances where the Medicare insurance company offering your Medicare Supplement policy pulls out of a state or a county and simply no longer offers the product.

However, Medicare Advantage plans are much less stable in that Medicare insurance companies add and delete plans all the time. Because Medicare Advantage plans are offered and renewed by Medicare on an annual basis (January 1—December 31), premiums, benefits, networks, and drug formularies change every year. What can also change every year is the actual plans being offered in your particular county of residence. While the Medicare Advantage plan can't single you out and cancel your individual coverage, they can decide not to renew the plan for the next year, which leaves you in a lurch, searching for a new plan for the following year. *This is known as a Plan Exit.*

That's a big deal. **In my opinion, you want your insurance premiums to be stable, you want your benefits to be stable, and you want your insurance company to be able to pay the bills when they come due. Wild swings in benefits and premiums can be annoying at best but could be a precursor to financial problems with the insurance plan or company at worst.** Most importantly, you want to make sure the Medicare Advantage plan you're on has a low likelihood of being canceled with a Plan Exit by the Medicare insurance company.

How do you predict this? You can't. Just because you're enrolled in a Medicare Advantage plan with a big brand name doesn't make you immune to the company possibly canceling or not renewing a Medicare Advantage plan via a Plan Exit. Just because you're with a smaller, less well-known company doesn't mean there's any guarantee either.

There are some really good, less well-known Medicare Advantage brands offering policies on a state or regional basis, too. The big national well-known Medicare insurance companies combined spend billions in advertising money every year to dominate the airwaves and send millions of pieces of direct mail out. That doesn't mean they're good or bad. They're just bigger and have much larger budgets. Small or mid-sized plans can offer just as good, worse, or better policies as the large, national plans.

## MEDICARE ADVANTAGE PLAN EXITS: HOW AND WHY DOES THIS HAPPEN?

There are lots of reasons, but it comes down to money. If the Medicare Advantage plan makes a reasonable amount of money for the Medicare insurance company, or they *think* that over time it will make money, they'll keep the plan. Sometimes they can't get enough doctors to accept their terms to be in-network. Sometimes they simply don't attract enough Medicare consumers to justify keeping the plan for sale. Lastly, if their margins are slim, or they end up losing money on the plan, they'll do a Plan Exit.

Some Medicare Advantage insurance companies do what's called in the industry "buying business." In that scenario, a new insurance company picks an area of the country they're not currently doing business in and decides to enter the market. To rapidly grow, they price their products lower than the competition and offer wonderful benefits—lower premiums, huge provider networks that are on-par or better than the competition, etc. So, of course, hundreds and thousands of Medicare consumers flock to these plans. Why wouldn't they? It's the best deal in town.

While that's a great recipe for selling insurance, sometimes the Medicare insurance companies underestimate their expenses. When that happens—to stem the financial bleeding, premiums go up and benefits decrease, sometimes rapidly. If they can't get them under control after a few years, they just pull out and leave the policyholders on the hook for finding a new Medicare Advantage plan during the AEP.

This doesn't happen with just the smaller, less-well-known insurance companies; the larger ones do it, too.

My advice? Make sure the Medicare Advantage plan you're considering has been around for a while. Ask your Medicare insurance agent for their opinion. Take a really hard look at any plans that are rated "Too New to Rate" on Medicare.gov because, well, they're *new*. Ask friends and neighbors. Make sure the Medicare insurance company offering the Medicare Advantage plan isn't a one-hit-wonder—here today, gone tomorrow. If the benefits are too rich or seem too good to be true, they might be buying business.

## OPTION 3: PROS AND CONS

## ALL MEDICARE ADVANTAGE PLANS MUST HAVE A MOOP!

This addresses Medicare Frustrating Flaw #1, which is that Original Medicare doesn't have an annual stopgap, a limit, or a Maximum Out of Pocket on how much you could potentially spend on your healthcare in a given year. Each Medicare Advantage plan must have an annual MOOP, or the bid from the insurance company won't be approved by Medicare. In 2021 and 2022, the maximum in-network MOOP is $7,550. Some plans obviously offer lower MOOPs than that, but none can make that number higher.

For HMO-POS and PPO plans which allow you to go outside of the network, the MOOP cannot exceed an annual maximum *combined* (in-network and out-of-network) MOOP of $11,300.

Remember, the MOOP is *only* for the medical portion, because the prescription drug benefit embedded in most Medicare Advantage plans has a separate schedule.

My actuary friends in the insurance industry have told me that less than 5% of all people on Medicare Advantage plans ever actually hit their medical MOOP during a calendar year. I can't find an official source online or in any type of research document to back that up, but it's easy to see how it's hard to do. That's because, for the majority of medical categories, the portion paid by the customer is a flat copay. For example, if your primary care physician co-pay is $5 for each visit, it would be awfully difficult to meet a $5,000 annual MOOP. You'd have to see your doctor 1,000 times in a year in that scenario. Even if you were hospitalized, most Medicare Advantage plans make the customer pay a copay for a certain number of days, and the total is usually nowhere near the MOOP. In instances where the benefit categories aren't a copay, it's usually some form of coinsurance no greater than 20% of the charges in-network. However, in instances where you're hospitalized multiple times a year, have a number of outpatient procedures or surgeries, and are prescribed very expensive drugs covered under Part B of your Medicare Advantage plan, you might hit the MOOP.

Quick math—if 24,000,000 people use Medicare Advantage plans for their Medicare coverage and 5% of those hit their MOOP in a year, that's 1,200,000 people. You could be one of them, which is exactly why it's there and why it's important to find a plan with the lowest MOOP possible.

##  EXTRA COVERAGE NOT AVAILABLE IN ORIGINAL MEDICARE OR MEDICARE SUPPLEMENTS

This is Medicare Frustrating Flaw #3, and here's where Medicare Advantage plans really shine. Medicare Advantage plans are allowed to build into their plans and provide coverage for a whole array of additional health-related services not offered through Original Medicare. Consequently, Medicare Supplement plans, because they only pay the leftover of what Original Medicare doesn't pay, can't offer these additional add-on features and benefits. The most popular add-on benefits are dental insurance, vision, and hearing aid dollar allowances, free gym memberships, and dollar allowances for over-the-counter items at specific retail shops (like CVS or Walgreens) or via mail-order.

This means you can actually use your health insurance when you're *not* sick! You can use your health insurance to *stay well* and maintain your health.

Here's a list (again) of extra benefits Medicare Advantage insurance companies can offer as a part of their insurance plans that are not offered or covered by Original Medicare, or Option 2: Original Medicare + Medicare Part D Prescription Drug + Medicare Supplement plan.

- ✓ Private hospital room or private nursing in the hospital
- ✓ Healthy food dollar amount allowances at grocery stores
- ✓ Adult daycare visits and personal home helpers
- ✓ Lifestyle drugs, including erectile dysfunction prescriptions
- ✓ Air Conditioner allowances for people with COPD and asthma

- ✔ Transportation to doctor's appointments

- ✔ Nutritional programs, personal trainers, and access to spas

- ✔ Grocery delivery

- ✔ Flexible dollar amount allowances for healthcare-related items at select retailers (sometimes in the hundreds of dollars per year)

- ✔ Acupuncture and massage therapy

- ✔ Gym memberships or fitness classes

- ✔ Weight management programs

- ✔ Dental insurance and dentures

- ✔ Routine eye exams and glasses

- ✔ Routine hearing tests and hearing aids

- ✔ In-home safety assessments and services

These extra benefits (Medicare insurance companies and Medicare agents call them "Value-Added Benefits") vary widely from company to company and plan to plan, so it's important to pay attention to the details. For instance, some plans only cover preventive dentistry—cleanings and fillings. Others cover preventive and comprehensive dentistry. It's rare these embedded benefits cover expensive items like crowns, bridges, implants, and dentures, but some do. It's smart to ask.

**Also, pay attention to the *type* of dental insurance benefit it is.** Some benefits only offer a certain dollar amount as an annual *allowance*, which means you'll have to pay your dentist upfront and then file a claim with the insurance company to get reimbursed. Yuck. Others operate like an HMO or PPO plan, and some don't have a network and let you see any dentist, and the dentist does all the paperwork and sends it in to get paid by the insurance company. You want your dental insurance benefit to *not* make *you* pay the entire bill upfront and then have to submit your own claim paperwork to the insurance company. So, make sure you dig into those details or ask your Medicare insurance agent about it.

Last point on dental: make sure you get the most annual allowance you can. Some plans only offer a $500 annual benefit, and I've seen plans that allow a $3,500(!) annual benefit. Yes, insurance companies usually change those amounts every year because they know it's a selling feature people look at. It's also one of the first things they cut if their plan isn't financially performing as they thought it would. **I'd shoot for a minimum of $1,500 annual dental allowance, to include dentures and implants, if you can.**

##  LOW OR $0 COPAYS FOR DOCTOR VISITS

Medicare Advantage plans make it easy and cheap for you to go to your doctor. In fact, the entire industry is moving towards lower and, in many instances, $0 copays to see your Primary Care Physician (PCP) as many times as you like during the year.

## LOW OR $0 PREMIUMS

There are many $0 plan offerings in the market today, which is fantastic. Although you still have to pay your Medicare Part B premium every month (with Medicare Supplements, too), this means you get medical and prescription drug coverage for a $0 monthly premium. It sounds fantastic, and for a heck of a lot of people, it is. Think about it—if you stay on Option #1: Bare-with-Medicare (Original Medicare + Medicare Part D Prescription Drug Plan), you still have to buy a Medicare Part D Prescription Drug Plan. There are no $0 Part D plans on the market, and there never have been. This will cost you at least $8 per month, probably more. If you go with Option #2 (Original Medicare + Medicare Part D Prescription Drug + Medicare Supplement plan), you'll spend anywhere between roughly $100-$250+ per month in premiums. $0 monthly premiums are a very attractive alternative.

Remember when I explained how Medicare Advantage plans can cost $0 per month? Well, you may also hear about so-called Medicare Advantage Part B Giveback plans. These plans go a step further and credit you back a portion or all of your monthly Medicare Part B premium. Yes, they're allowed, and they're getting more popular. Here's all I'll say—check the benefits to see how good they are compared to a $0 Medicare Advantage plan. I'm going to guess they'll be significantly better on the $0 plan. Also, ask how long the plan has been offered for sale. I've seen a number of instances where an insurance company sells this kind of plan and then cancels it a year or two later. Remember when I said Medicare Advantage plans usually make around 1-4% in margin? It gets very difficult to achieve that when you're crediting back Medicare Part B money to the person who enrolled in it.

## CHRONIC CONDITION MANAGEMENT

Only Medicare Advantage plans have care management programs to specifically work with people with chronic conditions like high blood pressure, diabetes, heart failure, end-stage renal disease, rheumatoid arthritis, depression, and more. Treatment plans for these conditions usually involve a case manager, health coaching, medication therapy management, and more. These teams of doctors and nurses employed by or contracted with the insurance company work with individuals on their Medicare Advantage plans to make sure they're doing their treatment, seeing their doctors, taking their prescribed medications, and, essentially, keeping them healthy. Not only is the Medicare Advantage plan insurance company required to provide these services, but they're also financially incentivized to do so by way of the Medicare Stars program. Medicare Advantage insurance companies measure how good of a job they do managing the health of people in terms of the following categories:

- ✔ Care for older adults – medication reviews
- ✔ Osteoporosis management in women who had a fracture
- ✔ Diabetes care –eye exams, monitoring kidney disease and controlling blood sugar.
- ✔ Controlling blood pressure
- ✔ Rheumatoid arthritis management

- ✅ Reducing the risk of falling
- ✅ Improving bladder control
- ✅ Medication reconciliation post-hospital discharge
- ✅ Statin therapy for patients with cardiovascular disease

Additionally, the CHRONIC Care Act passed in 2018 allows Medicare Advantage insurance companies to begin covering services like adult daycare, support for family caregivers, pest control, or other items to help people maintain or improve their health. Before this, insurance companies were allowed to deliver meals to people only after they'd been discharged from the hospital. Now, they can provide meals at any time if they think it could help keep people out of the hospital.

Medicare Advantage plans can opt to pay for benefits like healthy meal delivery (e.g., low-salt dinners for those with heart failure), transportation to the pharmacy or grocery store, home modifications to accommodate walkers and wheelchairs, and other services that may promote health but are not strictly medical in nature. (Sources: PrepareforMedicare.com/sources).

## 👍 NO HEALTH QUESTIONS

With very few exceptions, all Medicare Advantage plans must accept your application regardless of health status. As long as you sign up during the right timeframes, you can't be denied coverage, no matter how many or few health conditions you had or have.

## 👍 ONE INSURANCE PLAN, ONE INSURANCE COMPANY, ONE CARD

The vast majority of Medicare Advantage plans are MAPD plans, which, as previously noted, include medical and Part D prescription drug coverage. That means you only use one insurance card at the pharmacy, doctor's office, hospital, outpatient clinic—everywhere. You don't have to keep two (Option 1: Bare-with-Medicare = Original Medicare + Medicare Part D Prescription

Drug Plan) or even three (Option 2: Original Medicare + Medicare Part D Prescription Drug + Medicare Supplement plan) cards in your wallet or purse.

## EXCESS CHARGES

As you recall, this is Medicare Frustrating Flaw #2, which is used by many insurance companies and insurance agents as a reason to buy a Medicare Supplement plan G (or F, if you turned sixty-five before January 1, 2020). Medicare Advantage plans only partially solve this problem, so it's not really a Con, but it's also not a Pro. If you stay in your Medicare Advantage networks, you won't be subject to Medicare Excess charges because, by default, the contracted doctors, hospitals, and other medical providers must accept Medicare to get claims payments from Medicare Advantage insurance companies. If you have a PPO or an HMO-POS and go out of network *and* for some reason, that doctor doesn't accept Medicare Assignment, you may pay the full amount of the excess charges.

## BENEFITS CHANGE EVERY YEAR

Since Medicare Advantage insurance companies must submit their bids to Medicare annually, that means the benefits of your Medicare Advantage plan can change every year. They can get better than the prior year. They can get worse than the prior year. I can tell you from personal experience, it's downright rare for a Medicare Advantage plan to have the exact same benefits every year. In fact, I'm not sure I can remember a time when I was designing Medicare Advantage plans during the bid process when a plan *didn't* have benefit changes every year. Sometimes monthly premiums rise, too. All this means you've got to pay attention and read the plan documents you get on or around October 1 of every year. This plan document is called the Annual Notification of Change (acronym ANOC, pronounced A-knock), and it will have a section in it that compares the prior year's coverage to the coverage changes in the new year. I cover this in the Medicare Housekeeping (Chapter Ten) in more detail.

**Pay attention to the following categories: Inpatient Hospitalization, your Primary Care and Specialist doctor's copays, lab benefits, outpatient benefits, MOOP, and deductibles. MOOPs can go up, and they can go down.** Lately, more and more insurance companies are introducing deductibles on medical *and* prescription drugs. Watch to see if your inpatient hospitalizations would make it more expensive for you to be admitted to the hospital. The same goes for lab, outpatient, and doctor's copays.

## MONTHLY PREMIUMS CAN FLUCTUATE WILDLY

I've seen $0 plans go to $40 from one year to the next. I've seen those $40 plans go to $50 the next year, then back down to $40 the following, then to $20 the next, then right back to $40. Some insurance companies do not put a priority on keeping their monthly premiums stable year-to-year, and some do.

## LACK OF PLAN CHOICES

Medicare Advantage insurance companies focus on areas with a lot of potential customers, which means they're largely centered around metropolitan areas. As I've covered earlier, that means that sometimes Medicare Advantage plan offerings in rural counties can be drastically less—or even non-existent. In fact, according to Kaiser Family Foundation, as of 2021, there are eighty-two counties in the United States (out of 3,006) where there are no Medicare Advantage plans available.

## TOO MANY PLAN CHOICES

Sometimes, the opposite is true; as I've also covered, there are certain areas of the country that have over fifty Medicare Advantage plan options to choose from.

## YOUR PLAN CAN GET CANCELED!

Technically, they can't cancel *you*. But Medicare Advantage insurance companies can simply cancel *the plan you're on* at the end of the year, leaving you to scramble to find a new one by the deadline. They do it all the time. Why would they do that? There are a lot of reasons, but the most common are: not enough people bought the plan, the plan is losing gobs of money, or they lost contracts with key doctors or hospitals in their PPO or HMO networks and can't meet network adequacy requirements to be able to file their bids with Medicare for the next year.

If this happens to you, the Medicare insurance company will announce this somewhere on or after October 1, right around the Annual Election Period (AEP), by sending you a letter. Medicare also sends a letter to you.

## NETWORKS

All Medicare Advantage plans (except very rarely-offered PFFS, private-fee-for-service plans, and MSA plans) come with networks—HMO, HMO-POS, or PPO. Don't assume your doctor will accept your Medicare Advantage plan even if they accepted the same brand name from your Affordable Care Act (ACA) plan or your employer-based insurance. They're separate contracts.

## PROVIDER DIRECTORIES ARE OUTDATED OR WRONG

It's commonly known in the health insurance industry that printed network directories are outdated almost as they're being printed. This is because doctors, hospitals, and other medical providers are constantly being added or eliminated from networks. Network directories are also often wrong on the insurance company's website, which is a bit hard to understand as online provider directories theoretically should be easy to update in real-time. Nevertheless, Medicare audited several insurance companies between 2016 and 2018, and here's what they found:

*48.74% of the provider directory locations listed had at least one inaccuracy.* Types of inaccuracies included:

- ✓ The provider was not at the location listed.

- ✓ The phone number was incorrect.

- ✓ The provider was not accepting new patients when the directory indicated they were.

The problem has gotten so bad that Medicare put new regulations into place in 2018 that could fine insurance companies up to $25,000 per customer for errors in their Medicare Advantage plan directories. (Sources: PrepareforMedicare.com/sources).

## HMOS USUALLY REQUIRE REFERRALS

In typical HMO plans, your primary care physician acts as your gatekeeper. That means they must refer you to specialists or other medical professionals; you can't just open your network directory and choose a specialist—you've got to get permission from your PCP first.

## HIGH PPO OUT-OF-NETWORK COST-SHARING AND MOOPS

While I'm a big fan of Medicare Advantage PPOs, mainly because they don't restrict you to only using the providers in the plan's network like HMOs, you've got to watch your out-of-network benefits. Many times, the costs of going out of network if you have a Medicare Advantage plan that allows it, can cost you more money than simply remaining Bare-with-Medicare! For example, an in-network PCP copay might be $10, but if you go to a PCP out-of-network it might charge you 30% to 40%, even 50% of the total charge, which is higher than the 20% coverage Original Medicare provides (after your Part B deductible).

Many Medicare Advantage PPO plans place high deductibles on their medical benefits if you go out-of-network. Out-of-network MOOPs can be very high, especially in PPO plans. If you're going the PPO route, make sure to pay special attention to the out-of-network benefits because they vary wildly depending on the plan and the insurance company offering them.

## MID-YEAR PROVIDER NETWORK CHANGES

If your doctor leaves or the insurance company cancels your doctor or hospital's contract in the middle of the year, you may have to find another provider in the network to treat you until you can switch Medicare Advantage plans during the AEP.

★ ★ ★ ★ ★

If you'd like to get an idea of which Medicare insurance companies are big players in the Medicare Advantage insurance space, head over to the website at PrepareforMedicare.com/links.

## FINAL THOUGHTS

By this point, you should have a very good idea of the three coverage options you have to consume your Medicare benefits. If you're curious about it, you now have a pretty good basic understanding of how Medicare insurance companies make money on each product they're offering. Not only that, but you've got a lot to think about when it comes to which pros and cons of each option are important to you.

There's no doubt about it; Option 1 leaves some pretty large financial exposure gaps in your coverage. Option 2 covers those gaps and offers the most freedom and flexibility in terms of networks and travel freedom, but it certainly comes at a significant monthly premium cost. Option 3 is rapidly growing in popularity but has its own drawbacks that may keep you and your Medicare insurance company actively engaged in your insurance coverage more than you want. Hopefully, I've empowered you with the information you need to make the best choice for you.

Now that you've got a great primer of what's available to you, let's see what Medicare insurance companies and agencies want to sell you, and how they do it.

CHAPTER FIVE

# THE MEDICARE MARKETING MACHINE
## WHAT IT MEANS FOR YOU
## (AND HOW TO MAKE THE MOST OF IT!)

By now, you know there are essentially three paths to consuming your Medicare benefits:

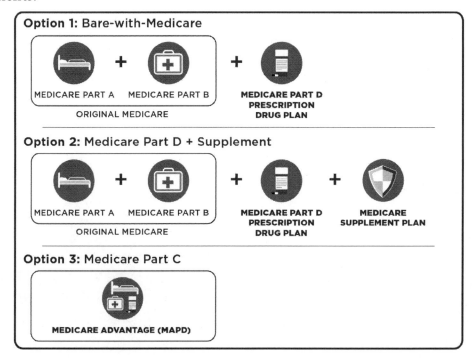

Each choice is a singular way of consuming your benefits, but each choice brings with it a series of additional choices—which plan(s) to buy, which you can qualify for, which you can afford, and which will meet your healthcare needs.

## WHICH PATH TO CHOOSE?

If you're still undecided or feeling confused, don't worry—that's a natural and common reaction. It's not scary; let's work through this together.

Throughout the previous chapter, I listed a number of pros and cons to each approach to help you think about what's important to you. I've done this because it's a common approach we're all used to. When we buy a new vacuum cleaner, read new car reviews, product-buying guides, or read a review online to help us decide which cell phone to buy, we all run across pros and cons whenever we check out reviews and product-buying guides. It's familiar to all of us.

But one of the problems with Medicare insurance is that there are no singular or popular ranking services out there. JD Power releases a list, but it's not widespread and leaves much to be desired. Medicare publishes a star rating which is supposed to be somewhat of a consumer ranking guide for Medicare Advantage and Medicare Part D Prescription Drug Plans, but as I cover in Chapter Two, it's far from perfect. As a result, in my opinion, the average Medicare consumer won't feel a bit of difference between a 3.5-star plan or a 4-star plan.

So, let's take a slightly different angle—away from a simple pros and cons approach. Let's step back and view the choices you have from a *marketing perspective*. After all, the insurance marketing industry is huge; they employ thousands of people and spend billions of dollars each year to get you to buy their products. So, let's take a look at how they segment you and why, because doing so might just help you decide which path to take when buying or changing your Medicare insurance coverage.

Why is this important? *Because insurance companies advertise insurance policies to you that they think you're most likely to buy, not necessarily the products you should buy.* However, as we'll see later in the chapter, they're often right, which is how they've been so successful in getting consumers to buy Medicare insurance policies. They probably know your buying tendencies, likes, and dislikes better than you do!

Why is this important? Because even though the Medicare insurance companies and Medicare insurance agencies have a lot of data on you, they only know what they know. They don't know whether you're healthy or sick. They don't know what prescriptions you're on. They don't know what your financial risk tolerance is—do you like to pay as you go, or do you prefer a pre-paid approach?

So, let's see what they do know and how they come to those conclusions as we dig into what Medicare insurance companies, insurance agencies, and professional marketers use to sell you Medicare insurance policies. *After all, if you understand both why they're doing it and how they're doing it, you can use this knowledge and perspective yourself. Knowing how they target you can help you decide the right coverage path choice and the right Medicare insurance policies for your specific needs.*

The first step in doing this is understanding that the goal of all of this advertising is to get you to engage with their company so they can sell you something. One of my favorite movies is the 1992 classic, *Glengarry Glen Ross*, in which Alec Baldwin's character says, "Guy don't walk on the (car) lot lest he wants to buy." The same applies here; all the Medicare insurance companies and agencies want you to do is call them or click an ad on a website. They essentially want you to "walk on the car lot," and engage them; they want you to begin a buying process. That relationship can't start until you call or click.

## MEDICARE MARKETING 101

Medicare insurance companies and agencies make more money by selling Medicare Advantage plans. That means as much as 80-90% of the advertising you're getting is going to relate to that product. That also means you're not going to hear much about Medicare Part D Prescription Drug Plans or Medicare Supplement plans on TV.

The big Medicare insurance companies, as well as the mid-sized or smaller ones, really hope to *sell* you their Medicare Advantage plans. Sure, they'll take a Medicare Supplement or Medicare Part D Prescription Drug Plan sale, but they really want to sell you Medicare Advantage. But of course, just because they're primarily advertising Medicare Advantage plans doesn't mean you have to buy one. It's what they want you to buy, not necessarily what's best for you.

**The vast majority of those marketing dollars are spent by the big Medicare insurance companies, like United Healthcare, Mutual of Omaha, Aetna, Humana, Cigna, Blue Cross and Blue Shield, and WellCare. However, there are hundreds of mid-sized or smaller Medicare insurance companies that have really good products—just not tens of millions of dollars to spend on marketing. Don't let that fact dissuade you from considering lesser-known, smaller Medicare insurance company products.**

What's more, if you ever decide to buy a Medicare Supplement or Medicare Part D Prescription Drug Plan, you'll be subtly (or not-so-subtly) asked over and over again to consider buying a Medicare Advantage plan. They'll do what's called re-marketing and try to upsell you into a Medicare Advantage plan. Again, that's because Medicare Advantage plans make the Medicare insurance company and their Medicare insurance agencies the most money. The direct mail won't stop, and neither will the phone calls from your current Medicare insurance carrier a few times a year, asking you whether or not you'd like to consider a Medicare Advantage plan. Simply ask them to take you off their phone list, and they must comply.

Medicare insurance companies and agency marketing professionals know what words and phrases Medicare consumers typically pay attention to. They know words like *choice* and *supplemental benefits* like *dental, eyewear*, and *gym membership discounts*, and *$0 premiums* attract your eyes and ears. All you have to do is watch any Medicare insurance company or agency TV commercial or peruse a direct mail piece to see at least two out of those three concepts presented.

Those marketing phrases or approaches aren't how you should prioritize your Medicare medical and prescription drug insurance needs; they're only a factor. But marketing professionals also know droning on about MOOPs and deductibles will bore their audience. Marketing professionals are trying to get you to click or call—not bore you to death—so they go with what will get you to take action.

That isn't to say or suggest they're doing anything wrong. All I'm suggesting is that when you're considering which path to take, you're probably not going to see all three Medicare options presented in a balanced way or given equal airtime.

Medicare marketers use celebrities and patriotism—lots of red, white, and blue—to stir your emotions, so you call or click. Sometimes they might even give their marketing pieces an "Official Medicare" feel.

As someone with years of Medicare marketing experience under my belt, I don't believe advertising is a bad thing. It's not evil. It's not manipulative. It's not dishonest. In fact, Medicare insurance advertising is highly regulated—any advertisement has to go through a pretty lengthy approval process from the insurance company and Medicare themselves. That's why you'll normally see all of the disclaimers in fine print on the bottom of the Medicare insurance advertising you see. The truth is companies can't outright lie or misrepresent their products.

Advertising is also, at this point, a fact of life. You can have the best product in the world, but if it's not marketed, no one will ever know about it.

There are three primary ways Medicare insurance companies can get you to consider buying their products: TV advertising, internet advertising, and direct mail. Marketing professionals use all three to generate what's called a *halo effect*. This is how Medicare insurance marketers get you to click or call.

All marketing people know it's highly unlikely that anyone calls a 1-800 number the first time they see a Medicare insurance commercial on television. It's also unlikely someone will see an internet ad and click it the first time they see it. It's similarly unlikely someone will call a 1-800 number or visit a website just by getting one piece of direct mail in their mailbox. However, put all three together—produce a TV ad, followed up by three or more pieces of direct mail in your mailbox, and show you internet ads during the same period—and that's called a marketing *campaign*. They know you're way more likely to click or call on *one* of those ads if your brain has seen or heard it multiple times, so they use multiple approaches over time – a *halo effect*.

It's not just insurance companies advertising, either. Large insurance agencies who hope to sell you something and capture a commission from the insurance companies also advertise around the clock. It's sometimes hard to tell the difference between the two. But it's safe to say if you see a branded advertisement, it's probably a Medicare insurance company. In other words, if you see an ad for United Healthcare, if you call a 1-800 number or click an internet ad, it'll likely take you to a captive United Healthcare sales representative or website you can purchase insurance through. If you see a generic Medicare insurance ad with no Medicare insurance company branding, it's generally safe to say it's a Medicare insurance *agency* advertising. Calling or clicking will take you to an independent Medicare insurance salesperson or sales website for a Medicare insurance *agency*, not a Medicare insurance company salesperson. More on the differences between captive and independent agents in Chapter Eight.

## TV ADVERTISING

Marketing professionals use TV primarily for brand awareness—which is to say, they familiarize you and your brain with their brand. Again, they don't expect a large percentage of you to call the number on your screen, although some do. Companies use TV to get you familiar with their company and brand, so when you see another ad on your computer screen, you click it. Or you see that TV ad so many times, it eventually wears you down, and you call their 1-800 number.

Spend any time watching Fox News, MSNBC, CNN, the Golf Channel, COZI, or any other channel with a high percentage of Medicare-aged viewers, and you have probably seen multiple TV commercials on Medicare insurance, especially around the September-December timeframe. That period coincides with the Annual Election Period (AEP), which is when the entire Medicare population can buy different plans for the upcoming year.

If you're streaming anything online—Hulu, Amazon Prime—any internet-based streaming service that displays ads, they very likely know your age. So, when it's time for a commercial, they can pinpoint what products you'll most likely buy using your age, viewing, and buying habits.

Increasingly, many companies have been hiring celebrities to pitch their products. By now, you've probably seen ads using paid spokespeople—ex-NFL quarterbacks, Olympic athletes, or D-list Hollywood celebrities to entice you to call or click. Of course, there's nothing wrong with that. Celebrity endorsement is a tried-and-true method of generating sales leads.

## INTERNET ADVERTISING

In some respects, online advertising is the Wild West of marketing. Imposter third-party lead aggregators use brand names to spoof real insurance company websites and then sell your data to others. Most of the time, these imposters don't have permission to use the Medicare insurance company's brand name in their advertising but do it anyway. This is why I repeatedly note in this book that **clicking on random websites and Google ads will lead you down various rabbit holes of frustration and incorrect information. I strongly suggest you avoid doing this.** To help you, I've got a whole section of my website dedicated to the *correct* links to reputable and well-known Medicare insurance company and Medicare insurance agency websites. Those can be found at PrepareforMedicare.com/links.

Medicare insurance companies compete for ad space with the Medicare insurance agents and agencies who sell products for the same Medicare insurance companies. Outside of Medicare insurance company corporate websites, it's generally a pretty good rule of thumb that any internet ad or website with a *.com* behind the website address wants to sell you something, gets paid a commission to sell you something, or sells your information to someone who does.

Using Google, Bing, Facebook, Instagram, and other social media platforms to advertise to you is not new, but the adoption of this as a major advertising outlet for people on Medicare has increased exponentially over the last few years. According to Pew Research, 40% of people ages sixty-five and over regularly use social media like Facebook and Instagram.

All the proof you need is right in your internet browser. Google the word Medicare and at least four ads will pop up before the first organic result is displayed. That placement on your Google search results is paid for by either insurance companies or insurance agencies who make commissions off insurance policy sales.

Right after those ads, you'll usually find an organic link, which means its placement is *not* paid for, displaying the government's Medicare website, Medicare.gov, followed by the government's Social Security website, www.ssa.gov. Look a little further down on the first page of your Google results, and you'll probably notice a map advertising companies or insurance agents who have paid for that placement as well. Look to the right of the page, and you'll get even more ads.

Facebook advertising is also a huge way Medicare insurance companies and Medicare insurance agencies get you to call or click. Facebook knows everything about you, too. They certainly know your age, and advertisers can target ads specifically based on that and other data points. Medicare insurance companies and Medicare agencies sometimes pay Google, Bing, Facebook, and other internet companies upwards of $50 for each click should you click that advertisement.

## DIRECT MAIL

If TV is for branding, internet advertising is used to target the 40% of the sixty-five-and-over population using social media and 80% of the people in that age group doing online Medicare research. The third installment of the halo-effect Medicare insurance marketing strategy is using direct mail. It's widely considered the workhorse of the group. It's cheaper than TV and often cheaper than internet advertising, and it's a tried-and-true method. It's worked for decades and remains a very effective way of marketing and generating sales leads.

I love getting the mail. Call me crazy, but for me, there's something fun about walking to the mailbox every day and opening it. Sometimes I'm surprised to find that someone has sent me a check for a rebate I mailed in three months earlier and forgot about. Sometimes I get a holiday card from an old friend. When I get a utility bill, I'm always eager to open it to see if I spent more or less than the prior month. Sometimes I get coupons for things I want to buy. But most of the time, the direct mail goes straight in the trash.

There's a science to direct mail. Well, let's call it equal parts science and psychology. The goal of *all* direct mail is to get you to take action. First, they want you to open it. The envelopes are designed to be slightly mysterious—what's inside? Often, they're designed to look like official government correspondence. Sometimes they come with complex instructions for how you're supposed to open them (for example, 1. Fold here, 2. Fold there, 3. Fold and open here), which is supposed to pique your interest. Marketers want your brain to think, *What possible wonderful thing could be inside this piece of mail that's clearly so important it comes with opening instructions?*

If they don't come with envelopes, they're usually postcards (which are cheaper to produce and mail) that have ad copy specifically designed to catch your eye and interest in milliseconds. They want your brain to pause—just for an instant—before throwing it in the trash. If it does, marketers know you're likely to at least glance at it and remember the brand name before it goes in the recycling bin. They know that you will likely store that brand image and name away somewhere in the back of your mind. You might even see a TV commercial later for that same brand and take action then, without even remembering you previously saw it on a direct mail piece.

If these marketers first succeed in getting you to open the envelope or read the postcard—even for a millisecond—they know they have a better chance of getting you to call the 1-800 number or visit a website. If you do, you are counted as a "lead," and the marketers get to count you as a win. That's because you interacted with the direct mail piece.

Marketers tirelessly tweak their ad copy. Which wording worked best? How many calls into the 800-number did a particular piece of direct mail generate? How many website visits were there?

## PERSONALIZED MEDICARE MARKETING IS HERE

But have you ever stopped to wonder why we get so much direct mail? Have you ever stopped to think about why you get the *type* of direct mail you get? Did you know your next-door neighbor may not get the same exact direct mail as you do?

Why is it you seem to see the exact same type of TV product advertising over and over?

What about internet ads? Why do certain ads pop up in your internet browser time and time again? Ever wonder why the ads that pop up on your computer screen or in your search results sometimes seem to be based on the websites you've previously visited? How on earth did they know you live where you live? Are they tracking you?

**Yes.**

How do they do this?

Have you ever taken out a car loan? Applied for or have a credit card? Filled out an online survey? Bought a set of tires? Own your home? Pay property taxes? Have a Facebook account? LinkedIn? Have you ever Googled your name? Amazing what pops up, right? How do they get that information?

Lots of the data about you on the web is public, or somewhere along the way, you've joined a membership site, entered your information on a website, or signed up for a product and unwittingly given your information to the companies, which then turn around and sell it. You've contributed to this process, whether you remember agreeing to it or not.

The rise of the internet over the last twenty-five years has brought this kind of data tracking into the spotlight. But this has been done for decades, well before Google and Facebook. Years ago, if you subscribed to a *JC Penny, Car and Driver*, or an *LL Bean* catalog, it said something about you, and that information was tracked and sold.

There are huge companies—names you've never even heard of—that gather information from everywhere, combine it, crunch it through special algorithms, and sell the result to other companies.

They know how old you are. They know where you live. They know your approximate net worth. They know what kind of car you drive, whether you're a Democrat or a Republican, a cat or dog lover, if you mow your lawn or hire it out, and whether you subscribe to a certain magazine, newspaper, or online membership. They know if you carry credit card debt or are debt-free. All of this says a lot about you, your health status, your preferences, your income, your budget, your temperament, your likes and dislikes.

This is exactly why—almost like clockwork—every Medicare insurance company in the country fills up your mailbox starting at age sixty-four and won't stop.

But they don't just fill up that mailbox and your Google search results or web browser with general information—oh, no. They might know you better than you know yourself! You might get an ad for a Medicare Supplement. Your friend might get an ad for a Medicare Advantage PPO plan, whereas your other friend might get a Medicare Part D Prescription Drug Plan all from the same company. Why?

All companies who spend money on marketing do what's called segmentation. If there are more than sixty million people on Medicare, there's simply no way companies can afford to mail or market to everyone on Medicare. So, they don't. They pick and choose who they market to based on hundreds, if not thousands, of data points. This is why your neighbor probably gets a different Medicare direct mail ad than you do. It's called *segmentation*. Why do certain TV commercials end up on Fox News but not CNN? Segmentation. Why do you hear a certain commercial on sports talk radio but not on the local rock station? Segmentation.

So, how are you segmented by Medicare insurance companies and Medicare insurance agencies? First of all, they're going to buy and use those lists to send you advertisements for certain products because they believe you're a "likely buyer" of that product. Do you make a million dollars a year? You're more inclined to buy a certain product. Do you rent a home? You're inclined to buy a different product. Are you seventy-five or sixty-five years old? Again, different product. Do you subscribe to a magazine that caters to healthy living, cooking at home, running, or working out? You're going to be inclined to buy a different product.

Like it or not, you're categorized into buckets of potential customers, and that's how they market to you.

**Let's take a look at what these marketing professionals and marketing agencies *think* you should buy and turn it around: how can we use this approach so *you, the Medicare consumer*, can decide which path makes sense for you to take?**

# SEGMENTATION

## HOW MARKETING PROFESSIONALS TARGET YOU, AND WHAT WE CAN LEARN FROM IT

Marketers have been segmenting populations since the dawn of advertising. They're getting better and better at it, using more and more data. Segmenting the baby boomer generation has become equal parts science and art, and many people and firms have attempted it over the last twenty years due to the generation's purchasing power—it's the wealthiest generation in the history of our country. Therefore, many companies want them to buy their products, including, of course, Medicare insurance companies.

There were approximately seventy-eight million boomers born between 1946 and 1964. They normally get segmented into two different buckets—1946-54 and 1955-64.

Merrill Lynch did a study in 2005 and came up with five different segments:

**1** Empowered Trailblazers

**2** Wealth-Builders

**3** Leisure Lifers

**4** Anxious Idealists

**5** Stretched and Stressed

The American Association of Retired Persons (AARP) does it, too. Here's a sampling of how they've labeled certain sixty-five and over segments:

**1** Overwhelmed and Unfortunate

**2** Active and Successful

**3** Positive and Responsible

**4** Regular Folk

**5** Fortunate and Ready

**6** Alone and Ill

Sources: PrepareforMedicare.com/sources

I've seen this segmentation done a few different ways, from marketing agency presentations to industry seminars. Some have eight categories, some have six. I've broken it down into five, but let's get rid of the labels and talk about people.

## LISA

Meet Lisa. Lisa makes well over $80,000 per year. Lisa is a planner; she loves to read and research. She never makes big financial decisions without doing gobs of internet research and reading articles on the subject at hand. She likes feeling in control of her finances, and when she makes a choice, she's confident she made the right one because she did the research. Lisa is a seventy-five-year-old widow. She taught public school when she was younger but quit to raise her family while her husband worked. Unfortunately, her husband passed away some time ago, but he left her a good amount of life insurance to get the kids through high school and to help pay for college. Lisa went back to school to get an advanced degree and ended up working in public school administration for a decade. Later, she got her PhD and became a tenured college professor for several years until she retired at age sixty-seven.

Lisa has done a great job of saving money in her retirement accounts over the years, and she has to take annual distributions from those accounts. She also has several rental properties which generate cash flow. She gets two teacher's pensions which provide a healthy cashflow. She travels a lot with groups of people and close friends.

Lisa is on top of her finances. She works with a financial advisor who manages her investments, but her advisor is clueless when it comes to

Medicare coverage. She doesn't take any medications, doesn't have any history of major illnesses, and only goes to the doctor for routine checkups a few times a year. Since she has disposable income, she doesn't mind spending a little money to make sure she stays healthy. She belongs to the town swim club and swims three times a week, takes online Pilates via a monthly subscription, and belongs to the local gym. As evidenced by her advanced degrees, she's well-read. She takes free courses at the local university for fun and feels like she knows enough about Medicare to make good decisions.

Lisa doesn't think much of insurance agents, mostly because she's confident she can do all of the legwork herself. She doesn't mind doing research and actually finds it a bit fun, like a puzzle. She talked to friends and family, did hours of research online (most of which frustrated and confused her) and eventually purchased a Medicare Supplement plan G, which costs her $155 per month, along with a Medicare Part D Prescription Drug Plan to cover her prescriptions for an additional $30 per month. That's because Lisa doesn't want to be bothered by having to see doctors in a network. She also doesn't want anyone helping to manage her healthcare, as she feels completely comfortable doing the research herself. Lisa doesn't have any dental insurance because she doesn't think the premiums are worth it. So, when she goes to the dentist, she just pays with cash. The same goes for her eyewear and contact lenses; she thinks she gets a great deal at her local big box store and sees no need to have vision insurance. She feels good about her choices and reviews her coverage once a year in about fifteen minutes.

If you're like Lisa, you're what's considered rich in retirement. You're most likely going to purchase a Medicare Supplement plan G or N and a higher-premium Medicare Part D Prescription Drug Plan that has a large formulary and few, if any, deductibles and coinsurance.

A slight wrinkle to this—if you're like Lisa, you may also view a $0 premium Medicare Advantage PPO option as an alternative. Why spend money every month on a Medicare Supplement and a Medicare Part D Prescription Drug

Plan when you can get both in a Medicare Advantage PPO plan for $0 per month and have no network restrictions because it's a PPO? Remember, PPOs come with in-network *and* out-of-network benefits? Sure, the out-of-network benefits aren't typically very good, but if you do happen to go out-of-network, you have no problem paying the eventual bill at this income level. *This approach is a form of self-insurance*; instead of paying monthly premiums up-front for a Medicare Supplement and Medicare Part D Prescription Drug Plan to an insurance company, you might just want to keep that Medicare Supplement and Medicare Part D Prescription Drug Plan monthly premium in your pocket and save it for when you need to pay for medical services.

## LEROY AND BARBARA

Meet Leroy and Barbara. Leroy is sixty-seven, and so is Barbara. They live in Missouri. Leroy worked as the manager of a bookstore his whole life, and Barbara worked as an administrative assistant. Together, they raised two successful kids and put as much money away as they could. They still live in the same house they bought thirty-five years ago, have no mortgage, and retired a few years back. They really don't travel much, other than the occasional Missouri winery trip and to see the grandkids in Washington, D.C. Leroy noodles around on the internet, buying and selling rare books when he finds them. Between Leroy's rare book sales, Social Security, and their retirement accounts, their annual income is between $60,000 and $80,000 per year.

Leroy and Barbara don't have a financial advisor, but they do have a combination of 401(k) and IRA money sitting in low-cost mutual funds their son told them to buy years ago. They don't derive any pleasure from making financial decisions, and they haven't re-balanced their portfolio in decades. However, there's a decent amount of money sitting in those accounts from the steady contributions they made to them during their working years. With the right budget and planning, that should get them through their retirement years.

Leroy and Barbara both seem to be in okay health, but they're worriers. They haven't kept up with doctors' appointments; they take walks around the neighborhood but aren't particularly active; and they could probably stand to lose a few pounds. Compared to their peers, they're in decent shape and try to remain active because they know it's important. They have conveniently ignored their birthdays so far, but dread is starting to creep in. *What if our health goes sideways? Will I have enough money to cover a major illness? What if the stock market crashes?*

They're both on Medicare Supplement plan G and have low-cost Medicare Part D Prescription Drug Plans. Their combined monthly insurance premium bills are about $350. Leroy is more internet-savvy than Barbara, so he's already familiar with Medicare.gov, subscribes to AARP, and reads their magazine every month. He thinks they can possibly save money on their monthly premiums but isn't sure where to go or what to do.

Together, they feel pretty confident about their level of Medicare knowledge, but they're still not sure they're on the right plan. They've heard about this thing called Medicare Advantage—some of their friends have those. They'd be open to discussing other options if it can save them a little money every month, but they're worried about the amount of coverage they provide. Still, they're willing to try new things. Both of them wear glasses and would like to have dental insurance to cover their annual checkups, but they don't know how to get it or whether or not it's worth it.

If you're like Leroy and Barbara, you're pretty well off. You're most likely going to purchase a Medicare Supplement plan G or N for between $130-$150 per month and a Medicare Part D Prescription Drug Plan, but a lower premium Part D Prescription Drug Plan between $8 and $25 that has a fairly restricted formulary and includes a deductible you must pay before benefits kick in. You might also be enrolled in a Medicare Advantage PPO plan that includes a Medicare Part D prescription drug card with relatively rich benefits and a monthly premium of between $40 and $80.

## NICK AND LAURA

Meet Nick and Laura. They're sixty-six years old and live outside of Chicago. They married young and immediately started a family. Nick worked in a blue-collar union job all of his life, and Laura spent about twenty years raising two kids before working as a bank teller. Nick retired with a small pension and some 401(k) savings, which is enough to cover their mortgage and bills, but without a lot left over. Laura is still working part-time as a bank teller to keep some income coming in, but she doesn't get any benefits. Between the two of them, they make between $40,000 and $60,000 per year.

Nick and Laura like to kayak together on the DuPage River and take walks in nature. They take their vitamins, but other than that, they don't spend a lot of time on their health. Nick is on blood pressure medicine, and Laura is an insulin-dependent diabetic. But so far, both conditions are managed well by their doctors and their prescriptions. Both of them have Medicare Advantage plans which include Medicare Part D prescription drug coverage, and premiums are $20 each per month. They don't spend a lot of time researching Medicare—mostly because it's boring and they don't find it to be all that important. They spent about an hour online doing research, got frustrated, and asked a friend who retired a year earlier for advice. That friend pointed them to an independent Medicare agent, and she helped them make a choice when they turned sixty-five. They're generally happy with it, stuck with it, and moved on with their lives. They can afford the premium, but not much more than what they're paying. Nevertheless, they are reasonably confident their agent placed them in a good plan.

Their Medicare Advantage plans also come with dental, vision, and hearing coverage, plus the plans cover acupuncture and a set number of meals delivered to their home if they are ever discharged from a hospital. They enjoy the gym membership they get with their Medicare Advantage plan. They're very unlikely to ever change their Medicare insurance plans, even if the premiums go up or the benefits get worse. In fact, they don't even read the annual notifications the insurance company sends; if they change something, they figure they'll just adjust and make it work. It works for them. They're generally happy with the level of coverage it provides. They like the balance of premium cost and coverage. If their agent ever suggested they make a change, they really wouldn't see much reason for doing so.

If you're like Nick and Laura, you're doing just fine in retirement. You probably have a Medicare Advantage plan, either an HMO or a PPO with a premium between $20 and $40 per month for each of you. You may also have access to a Group Medicare Advantage plan through a union, which might cost considerably more but might offer richer benefits.

## LUIS

Meet Luis. He's sixty-eight and lives in Tulsa, Oklahoma. He's been single for a while and makes between $25,000 and $35,000 a year in retirement. He lives within his means, wants for nothing, but there's not a whole lot left over at the end of the month. He likes to work on his car, does a little fishing, and is a DIY sort of guy. He thinks he's in good health. He eats what he wants, doesn't work out, and doesn't usually go to any doctors because he's never really been sick his entire life. He's a diabetic, but he manages it with his insulin shots and considers himself healthy.

Luis doesn't know much about Medicare. A few years back, he was introduced to a Medicare insurance agent from a friend in his apartment complex, and she signed Luis up for a $0 Medicare Advantage plan. He can't remember the name of the Medicare insurance company, but it works okay. He doesn't pay that much attention to his Medicare insurance coverage. Even if he thought about switching plans, he wouldn't be comfortable doing it on his own.

Luis would likely qualify for Extra Help or Low-Income Subsidies from the state or Medicare, but he hasn't applied.

If you're like Luis, you're most likely just scraping by financially in retirement. You have a $0 Medicare Advantage plan. If not, you're Bare-with-Medicare and have a low-cost Part D Prescription Drug Plan to help pay for your prescriptions.

## MARY

Mary lives in Boston. Mary is sixty-six and has had several different jobs over the years. Her last one was working for a cleaning service. She makes between $18,000 and $25,000 per year. Mary hasn't paid much attention to her health over the years, and, if she's honest, she knows she's a bit overweight and doesn't have the best eating habits. She is stressed out about getting older. She's very worried about getting sick. How would she pay her medical bills? Mary has struggled for years just to make ends meet, living paycheck to paycheck. She's got nothing put away for retirement, so the only income she gets is from Social Security.

Mary doesn't know anything about Medicare other than it's what you get when you turn sixty-five. At some point, she got a Medicare Part D Prescription Drug Plan in the mail, and she uses it for her two prescriptions at the local pharmacy. She doesn't know how she got it, but odds are, she's eligible for Low-Income-Subsidy and was automatically assigned a Medicare Part D Prescription Drug Plan by Medicare. She's spoken to a few Medicare insurance agents who have introduced her to $0 premium Medicare Advantage plans, but so far hasn't been able to make a decision and feels overwhelmed.

If you're like Mary, you're also a bit like Luis in that you're just scraping by financially. You're most likely going to use Original Medicare Plans A and B and add a Medicare Part D Prescription Drug Plan automatically assigned to you. Or you're most likely working with a Medicare insurance agent who has enrolled you on a $0 premium Medicare Advantage plan.

Again, the point of understanding how you're targeted by marketing professionals and segmented into advertising buckets is important to know for perspective. If the data indicates that you do not have much in retirement savings, you're not going to get many ads (if any) for Medicare Supplements. If you're rich, you may not get ads for $0 HMO Medicare Advantage plans.

And while there's plenty of data out there for marketers to use to target and segment you, they only know what they know. They don't know what your health situation is, what medications you're taking, or your financial risk tolerance. Only you can determine those.

Probably 80-90% of what you see in your mailbox, on TV, and online is going to revolve around Medicare Advantage. That's what they want your brain to remember. Fight the urge to take action until *you've* decided which path is *truly right for you*. Realize it's marketing; Medicare insurance companies and agencies aren't telling you everything because they can't fit all of that into a thirty-second TV commercial or on a postcard in your mailbox. Thus, they talk about big shiny things like choice, $0 premiums, and the extras like dental and vision because they know you like those things. They're using words you want to hear. They're doing this to get you to call them or click on a website link.

Resist the urge until you're ready. But also understand that what they're marketing to you is indeed what they think you should buy, based on what they already know about you. Maybe they're right! But you have to take all of this in and decide for yourself. Don't let marketing sway you one way or another. Ultimately, it's up to you.

# CHAPTER SIX

# BRINGING IT ALL TOGETHER AND FORMULATING YOUR PLAN
## MEDICARE ADVANTAGE VS. MEDICARE SUPPLEMENT

By now, you have a general understanding of Medicare, when and how you can enroll, the different paths you can take, and how you might be predisposed to select a path based upon your financial situation, health status, attitudes towards both, where you live, how long you've lived, and what healthcare benefits seem most important to you.

You've considered the pros and cons. You have also given plenty of thought to how you're marketed to, why you're marketed to, and how segmentation can help you decide what kind of Medicare consumer you are.

So, which one are you? Are you like Lisa, who has plenty of money and is actively engaged with her health management? Or are you more like Luis, or somewhere in-between like Leroy and Barbara?

If you fall somewhere in between, prioritize by income level. It's okay if you want to explore all three of these options, but it's important to have one preferred choice in mind. You don't have to decide just yet, but it's coming soon because there's more food for thought in the following pages.

# MEDICARE ADVANTAGE
## VS.
# MEDICARE SUPPLEMENT

### LET THE DEBATE BEGIN!

As a quick reminder, thus far, we've reviewed the three ways you can consume your Medicare benefits. Here they are again.

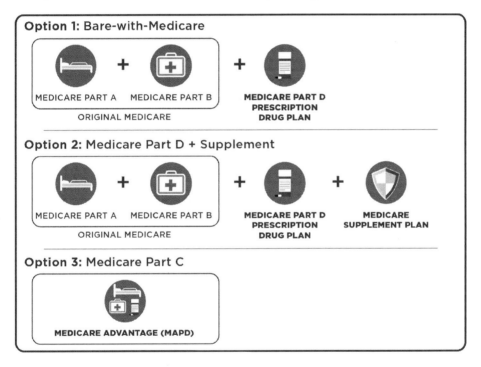

If you're new to Medicare, I'm betting that you are stuck debating whether or not Option 2 or Option 3 is best for you. That is, you're trying to decide whether you go with a Medicare Part D Prescription Drug Plan + Medicare Supplement or a Medicare Advantage plan.

If you've been on Medicare for a while, maybe you've noticed your Medicare Supplement monthly premiums are getting pricey, and the annual increases are noticeable. Perhaps you're in your mid- to late-seventies; they're getting downright expensive, right? This is right around the time folks revisit this debate—Medicare Supplement vs. Medicare Advantage.

I know, you're going back and forth. Which is better? Don't worry, it's not just you. This is a big debate among your friends, family, Medicare insurance agents, Medicare insurance companies, pundits, reporters, policymakers—just about everybody! So, which one is better?

Of course, you know my answer. It depends!

For me, I'm not a big fan of Bare-with-Medicare Option 1—not when Options 2 and 3 exist. There are just too many potential financial and coverage pitfalls leaving your Medicare coverage on Original Medicare Plans A and B. Millions of people who are Bare-with-Medicare can't all be wrong, so clearly it works for a lot of people. I just personally wouldn't allow those Frustrating Flaws noted in Chapter Three to enter into my Medicare insurance coverage when options to close those flaws (Options 2 and 3) exist. None of the three options are necessarily good or bad, but remember, you can't have a Medicare Supplement and a Medicare Advantage at the same time.

Which one should you choose? Neither answer is wrong, but you must choose one. Neither one is a bad choice; neither one is the right or best choice. It comes down to what works best for *you*. **What works for you might not work for your neighbor or your partner. It all depends on your preferences, health, and financial situation, which is why we spent so much time together demonstrating how others go about making the same or similar decisions.**

Here's another way to think about it. Medicare Supplements and Medicare Part D Prescription Drug Plans pay for items when you're sick, or they help you get better. When you go to the hospital, a Medicare Supplement helps pay the bill. When your doctor gives you a prescription, you use a Medicare Part D Prescription Drug Plan at your local pharmacy to fill that prescription.

Medicare Advantage plans do that as well, but because they can be built-in with so many additional options like gym memberships, OTC allowances, and healthy foods, you can use many Medicare Advantage plan features and benefits when you're *not* sick. That's a nice feature.

If money was no object, are you the type of person who prefers to spend $150-$280 or more per month predictably on a Medicare Supplement plus a Medicare Part D Prescription Drug Plan because they're easy to use, have only a few restrictions, and provide very comprehensive first-dollar coverage? Or would you rather buy a $0 Medicare Advantage PPO plan and keep that money in your pocket until you have to pay a copay or a deductible when you use the benefits?

Do you think the insurance company involving themselves in managing your healthcare is intrusive? Do you want to keep it simple and pay premiums only for medical and prescription drug coverage with no bells and whistles? Do you value convenience and saving time? You might like Medicare Supplements.

Do you like the idea of the insurance company helping your doctors and pharmacists coordinate your care and manage your chronic conditions all within one network or one group? Do you like the idea of a combination product—Medical plus Prescription Drugs that often come with dental, vision, hearing, OTC money allowances, transportation, and other benefits attached? Are you the type of person who wants to save money on premiums and pay as you go? You might like Medicare Advantage.

Are you a shop-and-save type of person, always looking for the best deal and enjoy the research and time spent finding that elusive needle in the haystack? Do you like shopping for the best plan every year? You might like Medicare Advantage.

Does the above sound like watching paint dry? Would you rather just set it and forget it, so to speak? You might prefer a Medicare Supplement.

See? I can't answer this Medicare Advantage vs. Medicare Supplement question for you, and neither can anyone else. All I can do is give you information and things for you to consider in order to help you arrive at the right decision. Confusion and frustration are completely normal and understandable when considering these two options. It's a choice almost every Medicare consumer grapples with at some point, especially because, as we've already seen, there are literally hundreds of insurance policy choices to make depending on where you live.

While you're mulling it over, here is some food for thought:

**First of all, if you're already over the age of sixty-five and don't have a Medicare Supplement Guaranteed Issue enrollment window, you may not even medically qualify for a Medicare Supplement plan if you've had prior**

**health problems or pre-existing conditions. The choice may have already been made for you.**

Second, can you afford your preferred option? If you currently have a Medicare Supplement and you're in your mid- to late-seventies, odds are your monthly premiums are getting very expensive and will continue to get more expensive the older you get. Can you continue to afford those premium increases?

Third, even if you can afford it, do you *want* to consume your Medicare via a Medicare Advantage plan or a Medicare Supplement plan? This is what I like to call the "Hassle Factor."

Lastly, if you choose Medicare Advantage or Medicare Supplement, what other factors or rule-of-thumb items should you keep in mind when shopping for coverage? As we've seen in the prior chapter, Medicare insurance companies, Medicare insurance agencies, and their marketers are masters at their craft. It's common practice to pick a feature or a benefit of any product and hammer it home in their advertising. "Oooh, look! This plan offers dental! This plan gives me $100 a year to spend on vitamins!" These aren't bad things. However, **don't let shiny objects blind you from achieving what should be your main goal, which is to get comprehensive medical and prescription drug coverage that meets your needs.**

# 1. QUALIFYING FOR MEDICARE SUPPLEMENTS

By now, you already know there are certain times when you can buy a Medicare Supplement and not have to answer health questions, and the insurance company has to accept your application. This is a one-time enrollment window to get a Medicare Supplement plan where the insurance company can't say no. This is generally when you first qualify for Medicare, normally around age sixty-five, but often later if you work past sixty-five. Either way, it expires six months after your Medicare Part B effective date. *Do not miss this window.* It's not impossible to get a Medicare Supplement after this window closes, but you'll likely have to answer health questions, and the insurance company may be able to deny you coverage.

If you have missed that window, even if you're on a Medicare Advantage plan and want to switch to a Medicare Supplement, you'll most likely have to answer these health questions. If you're healthy, it may not be an issue, but logic dictates the older you are, the more likely you are to develop health problems.

My point is if you're out of or don't qualify for Guaranteed Issue enrollment windows and think you want to go this route, be sure to submit your application on time.

If you have that open window coming up because you're turning sixty-five or retiring and have had major illnesses or surgery in your pre-retirement life, please look very long and hard at buying a Medicare Supplement if you can afford one. We all know cancer can come back. We all know heart problems don't normally just go away. If you don't get it during this open window, you most likely won't be able to get it in the future.

If you don't have an open window coming up, each Medicare Supplement insurance company has different rules and different medical questions. However, there are certain "kick-out" questions the majority of companies have that, if you answer yes to, automatically decline you. These generally have to do with whether or not you've been diagnosed or treated for any of the following conditions:

- Heart attack and other heart conditions
- Stroke
- Diabetes
- Lung disorders
- Prostate cancer
- Osteoporosis, arthritis, or other conditions that restrict mobility

Don't ever, ever lie on an insurance application, even just a little bit. If you do, and it's found out, they can retroactively terminate the policy, not pay the bills, etc. This is a big no-no. Said another way: always tell the truth.

I've said this earlier in the book, but it bears repeating. Never, ever cancel an existing Medicare Supplement policy without first confirming that a new Medicare Supplement policy has been issued or, if you're moving to a Medicare Advantage plan, confirming the new plan is in place. If you cancel your Medicare Supplement plan too early, they don't have to take you back.

## 2. AFFORDABILITY AND YOUR BUDGET

According to *US News and World Report*, the average Social Security benefit was $1,503 per month in January 2020. The maximum possible Social Security benefit for someone who retires at full retirement age was $3,011 in 2020 (Sources: PrepareforMedicare.com/sources).

### OPTION 3: MEDICARE PART C

**MEDICARE ADVANTAGE (MAPD)**

**I recommend that you do not spend more than 3% of your monthly gross income on a Medicare Advantage plan premium.**

Quick Math: this means, if you make the average Social Security benefit, you shouldn't pay more than $45 per month on a Medicare Advantage premium. I say 3% because, while Medicare Advantage plans typically include Medicare Part D prescription drug benefits, there are all sorts of copays that come with Medicare Advantage plans. You'll have copays, deductibles, and possibly coinsurance to pay for doctor's office visits, outpatient services, hospital services, ER visits, and your prescription drugs. This is also where the MOOP comes into play.

***My recommendation is that you don't purchase a Medicare Advantage plan with an annual MOOP any higher than $4,000.*** If you ever have a horrible health year and hit your $4,000 MOOP (unlikely, but possible), that will essentially be 25% of the annual average Social Security benefit.

There's another reason why I don't recommend purchasing a Medicare Advantage plan with a MOOP higher than $4,000. According to the Kaiser Family Health Foundation, when people on Medicare Advantage have an inpatient hospital stay of longer than three days, the out-of-pocket costs could surpass those of Original Medicare Part A. Said another way, people who are Bare-with-Medicare, which is Option 1, or Original Medicare + Part D Prescription Drug Plan, could pay less for that hospitalization compared to what they'd pay on a Medicare Advantage plan. That's because most Medicare Advantage plans charge a daily copay beginning on day one. In contrast, under Original Medicare Part A, when beneficiaries require an inpatient hospital stay, there is a deductible of $1,484 in 2021 (for one spell of illness) with no copayments until day sixty of an inpatient stay. *Nearly two-thirds (64%) of Medicare Advantage enrollees are in a plan that requires higher cost-sharing than the Part A hospital deductible in traditional Medicare for a seven-day inpatient stay, and more than seven in ten (72%) are in a plan that requires higher cost-sharing for a ten-day inpatient stay* (Sources: PrepareforMedicare.com/sources).

If you have additional income on top of your Social Security benefits, then obviously, the monthly premium can be higher than $45. Just do the quick math: use your calculator and multiply your monthly gross income before taxes by 0.03. That's the most I'd recommend you pay for a Medicare Advantage plan every month.

Truth be told, there are hundreds of $0 monthly premium Medicare Advantage plans out there across the country. Odds are, they exist where you live. The real sweet spot is to find one of those, preferably a PPO plan with an annual MOOP under $4,000. If you can't find a PPO, an HMO will still work—you've just got more legwork to do to make sure your doctors and hospitals are in the HMO network and potentially deal with tighter rules around which doctors and healthcare providers can see you.

## OPTION 2: ORIGINAL MEDICARE + MEDICARE PART D + SUPPLEMENT

If you choose this path, **I'm going to recommend that you spend no more than 8% of your monthly gross income combined between your Medicare Part D Prescription Drug Plan + Medicare Supplement plan.** I've raised that to 8% because the most popular Medicare Supplements (Plan F, G, and N) have minimal deductibles and copays to contend with. You're essentially paying more premium upfront to the insurance company. Therefore, they'll cover a larger portion of your healthcare bills if and when you need them to. If you buy a Medicare Supplement plan G, all you have to do is pay your annual Medicare Part B deductible, and then any other medical claim is generally covered at 100% for the rest of the year. This means you only have to pay your monthly Medicare Supplement insurance plan premiums and the Part B deductible, then you're done for the year.

Quick math: This means, if you receive the average Social Security benefit, you shouldn't pay more than $120 per month in premiums for your Medicare Supplement.

Truth be told, that's going to be hard to do if your only source of income is Social Security. That's why Lisa didn't bat an eye at those premiums, and most folks don't, as long as they have at least a decent amount of retirement income coming in on top of Social Security. It's generally safe to say that the wealthier you are, the more likely you are to go this route.

Typically, a Medicare Supplement plan G or N is going to cost you somewhere between $120 and $200 per month when you're sixty-five—and that amount will most likely go up every year as you get older. And don't forget, you still must buy a Medicare Part D Prescription Drug Plan, which on average, is right around $20 more. The Medicare Part D Prescription Drug Plans have a separate benefit schedule and have their own copays, coinsurances, and deductibles.

## AFFORDABILITY OVER TIME

How healthy are you? How long did your parents live? How long do you think you'll live? The other thing you'll want to consider around this topic is affordability over time. Since the introduction of Medicare Part D Prescription Drug Plans, the average monthly premiums for those policies have generally settled at around the $20-$25 mark. I wouldn't anticipate that to substantially increase above 1%-2% through inflation over the next twenty years.

Average Medicare Advantage plan insurance premiums seem to have actually leveled off or gone down since 2015. (Sources: PrepareforMedicare.com/sources). The average Medicare Advantage premium is $25 per month, although there are plenty of $0 options around.

However, the same can't be said for Medicare Supplement plans. I've already mentioned that Medicare Supplements generally increase in price the older you get while Medicare Advantage premiums are the same whether you're sixty-five or 105 years old. With Medicare Advantage, the Medicare insurance company can change monthly premiums every calendar year for everyone on that particular plan.

I've demonstrated this in the chart below. What I've done is provided a real-life example of Option 2: Original Medicare + Medicare Part D Prescription Drug + Medicare Supplement plan.

I've taken an example of a Medicare Supplement plan G from a major insurance company and inserted their 2021 rates by age. I've even taken the liberty of showing the lower-priced female rates because rates for males are typically higher. I've also shown the preferred rates, not the standard rates.

Then, I've added in the Medicare Part D Prescription Drug Plan so we can see a total monthly bill for the Medicare Supplement *and* the Medicare Part D Prescription Drug Plan premiums over time. I've even assumed a 3% annual price increase for the Medicare Part D Prescription Drug Plan.

Then, I've compared that to a Medicare Advantage plan's premium over time.

Even though Medicare Advantage plan monthly premiums generally haven't increased in the last five years, let's assume those premiums go up 3% a year as well, just to be fair.

Take a look:

Assuming a $25 per month Medicare Advantage premium when you're sixty-five . . .

| AGE | ANNUAL MEDICARE SUPPLEMENT PREMIUM | ANNUAL PART D PREMIUM | ANNUAL TOTAL | ANNUAL MAPD PREMIUM | ANNUAL TOTAL |
|---|---|---|---|---|---|
| 65 | $1,379 | $240 | $1,619 | $300 | $300 |
| 66 | $1,389 | $247 | $1,636 | $309 | $309 |
| 67 | $1,410 | $255 | $1,665 | $318 | $318 |
| 68 | $1,439 | $262 | $1,701 | $328 | $328 |
| 69 | $1,473 | $270 | $1,743 | $338 | $338 |
| 70 | $1,507 | $278 | $1,785 | $348 | $348 |
| 71 | $1,542 | $287 | $1,829 | $358 | $358 |
| 72 | $1,578 | $295 | $1,873 | $369 | $369 |
| 73 | $1,613 | $304 | $1,917 | $380 | $380 |
| 74 | $1,651 | $313 | $1,964 | $391 | $391 |
| 75 | $1,688 | $323 | $2,011 | $403 | $403 |
| 76 | $1,727 | $332 | $2,059 | $415 | $415 |
| 77 | $1,768 | $342 | $2,110 | $428 | $428 |
| 78 | $1,808 | $352 | $2,160 | $441 | $441 |
| 79 | $1,848 | $363 | $2,211 | $454 | $454 |

| AGE | ANNUAL MEDICARE SUPPLEMENT PREMIUM | ANNUAL PART D PREMIUM | ANNUAL TOTAL | ANNUAL MAPD PREMIUM | ANNUAL TOTAL |
|---|---|---|---|---|---|
| 80 | $1,890 | $374 | $2,264 | $467 | $467 |
| 81 | $1,934 | $385 | $2,319 | $481 | $481 |
| 82 | $1,976 | $397 | $2,373 | $496 | $496 |
| 83 | $2,021 | $409 | $2,430 | $511 | $511 |
| 84 | $2,064 | $421 | $2,485 | $526 | $526 |
| 85 | $2,124 | $433 | $2,557 | $542 | $542 |
| 86 | $2,169 | $446 | $2,615 | $558 | $558 |
| 87 | $2,215 | $460 | $2,675 | $575 | $575 |
| 88 | $2,261 | $474 | $2,735 | $592 | $592 |
| 89 | $2,308 | $488 | $2,796 | $610 | $610 |
| 90 | $2,353 | $503 | $2,856 | $628 | $628 |
| TOTAL ANNUAL INSURANCE PREMIUMS PAID YEARS 65-90 | | $56,388 | | | $5,868 |

Assuming a $115 per month Medicare Supplement premium when you're sixty-five, plus a $20 per month Medicare Part D premium ($135/month) . . .

The results of comparing a Medicare Part D Prescription Drug Plan + Medicare Supplement to a Medicare Advantage plan by premium over time are pretty stunning.

In this example, if you buy a Medicare Supplement and a Medicare Part D Prescription Drug Plan when you turn sixty-five and keep it until you die at age ninety, you'll pay *$56,000 in insurance premiums.*

The same scenario with a $25 per month premium Medicare Advantage plan? You've paid *only $5,800 in premiums over that same timeframe.*

Granted, Medicare Supplements provide more comprehensive medical payment coverage than Medicare Advantage plans do. The comparison above only measures annual insurance policy premiums.

But still, if you heed my advice and don't buy a Medicare Advantage plan with greater than a $4,000 MOOP, you could hit that catastrophic MOOP *level for thirteen of those twenty-five years* ($4,000 X 13 = $52,000) and still not have paid as much as just the Medicare Part D Prescription Drug Plan + Medicare Supplement premiums ($56,388). I'm not going out on a very long limb when I say it's impossible to hit a $4,000 MOOP thirteen years out of twenty-five and still be alive.

If they can afford it, many people like the simplicity and freedom Medicare Supplement plans provide. But examined over time, that freedom and simplicity certainly come at a cost. Can you afford that luxury? It's up to you. **If you can't comfortably afford the option of a Medicare Part D Prescription Drug Plan + Medicare Supplement plan, I'd urge you not to try.**

## 3. THE HASSLE FACTOR

### MEDICARE SUPPLEMENT PLANS

Medicare Supplement plans can be compared to something like a pre-paid Medicare insurance plan. If you buy a Medicare Supplement plan G, you're paying the insurance company a hefty premium every month to pay 100% of the bills after the Medicare Part B deductible. Once you've paid that deducible, generally that's it—you don't have to pay a penny more for any medical care for the rest of the year; the insurance company pays the rest. Medicare Supplements are as close to set-it-and-forget-it as you can possibly get in the Medicare insurance world. If you sign up at sixty-five or when you retire and pay the bill every month, they can't kick you off, and you never have to go shopping for it again if you don't want to.

This route is a bit of a hassle because you also have to buy a stand-alone Medicare Part D Prescription Drug Plan and really should shop that plan every year to make sure you've got the best deal. Plus, you've got to carry around three insurance cards in your pocket: your Red, White, and Blue Original Medicare card, your Medicare Supplement card, and your Medicare Part D Prescription Drug Plan card. True, not a big deal, but a bit of a hassle. Then, there are the premiums; they generally go up a little every year, so while the comprehensive medical coverage is nice from a financial planning perspective, it's annoying, to be sure.

## MEDICARE ADVANTAGE PLANS

Medicare Advantage plans can be compared to something like a pay-as-you-go Medicare insurance plan. Instead of paying the insurance company upfront for near-100% coverage, you're paying them less and keeping that monthly premium in your pocket—ready and waiting for when you have to use it. Yes, Medicare Advantage plans come with lower monthly premiums, but you'll pay a larger percentage of your medical bills out of pocket when you use that insurance. Medicare Advantage plans charge you a portion of the bill nearly every time you see a doctor, get a test, have outpatient surgery, or go to the hospital. That's why the MOOP is so important; you want it to be as low as possible so that every year, you have a limit on your medical financial exposure.

The first big hassle people with Medicare Advantage plans have is the network component. Are you opposed to working with your primary care physician to help you coordinate your care with other medical providers? What if your foot hurt and you wanted to make an appointment with a podiatrist directly, but you're told no—you must first go to your primary care physician? Do you hate the possibility of not being able to go to any doctor you want, when you want? Or are you willing to pay more out of pocket if you do go out of your network? Medicare Advantage provider networks change all the time; doctors come in and go out of the network, hospitals get into fights with insurance companies and cancel contracts . . . are you adaptable enough and okay with this potential hassle?

Medicare Advantage insurance companies are contracted by Medicare to offer plans one year at a time. This means the benefits, networks, and even monthly premiums change every year. I've yet to see an example of a Medicare Advantage plan that hasn't changed at least one benefit from year to year. This means you have to pay attention to insurance company paperwork sent to your house or email inbox every October and dig in to see what's changed. This is called an ANOC (Annual Notice of Change, explained in Chapter 10). If your plan benefits or premium substantially changed to the negative or something else changed (your favorite doctor left the network), then you'll have to shop all over again and enroll in a new plan during the AEP (Oct 15-Dec. 7). **It takes active management every year to make sure your Medicare Advantage plan will continue to meet your needs in the following year. You can't just put your head in the sand and expect that your plan will remain the same the following year.** Yet, according to a recent survey, 54% of Medicare consumers do not shop their coverage every year. This most likely means 54% of you aren't paying attention, and the plan you're on this year isn't the best deal—it might be worse or more expensive than the year prior, and you don't even know it. (Sources: PrepareforMedicare.com/sources).

Insurance companies offering Medicare Advantage plans also cancel plans all the time. Remember, they're contracted to offer these plans on an annual basis. They can't cancel or drop *you*, but they *can* cancel the plan you're on. They don't have to renew the plans every year, and when they don't, you'll get a letter from the company and from Medicare saying your plan is going away. If you don't select another Medicare Advantage plan, you'll drop back to Bare-with-Medicare Option 1: Original Medicare + Medicare Part D Prescription Drug Plan, and they'll automatically assign you a Medicare Part D Prescription Drug Plan if you don't select something else before January 1 of the new year.

Another hassle you could run into on a Medicare Advantage plan has to do with understanding what you'll potentially owe when you have medical claims. Many Medicare Advantage plan benefits, such as outpatient surgery, imaging, and lab work charge you a range of coinsurance. Often, the insurance company will pay a certain amount, leaving you some coinsurance to pay, usually 20% of the bill. Well, 20% of what? 20% of the bill, of course. Well, what's the bill going to be? You have no idea at the time of the test or procedure. An MRI at location A can be a different price at location B. Are you willing to shop around to see who charges the least amount? Shopping around the healthcare system for pricing is a major pain, takes a ton of time, and is difficult to understand. I think we all lament the fact that pricing isn't clear anywhere in the healthcare system. You don't have to shop around, and on a Medicare Supplement, it simply doesn't matter where you get your MRI as long as the provider accepts Medicare.

## 4. DON'T GET BLINDED BY SHINY OBJECTS

As I've mentioned previously, Medicare Advantage insurance companies are allowed to embed additional benefits within their plans that are outside of traditional medical and prescription drug benefits. Medicare Supplement plans are standard, so most can't include these extra benefits unless they're discounts or special programs outside of the actual insurance policy.

I think this is a wonderful feature and benefit of Medicare Advantage plans. Why wouldn't you want dental, vision, hearing, meals, acupuncture, and free transportation to and from your doctor's office if you can get it embedded within your Medicare Advantage plan? That way, you can use your health insurance to stay well *and* use it when you're not even sick!

From a marketer's perspective, I know many of the medical and prescription drug benefits found within all Medicare Advantage plans are mostly the same. Sure, the benefits vary, copays are different, hospitalization benefits are different, and those are very important. But every marketer worth their salt wants to find and highlight what's different or better about *their* product compared to anyone else's. That's why the sports celebrities currently hawking Medicare coverage on our TV screens, our direct mail, and internet ads all highlight these extra benefits because it's how they can show *their* plan is different from *other* plans. Can't you just hear them? "Get a plan with dental, vision, and hearing benefits! Call now!"

Again, this is a great feature of Medicare Advantage plans, no question. However, I'd urge you to exercise some restraint when considering the importance of these extras.

First of all, just because you choose a Medicare Supplement plan instead of a Medicare Advantage plan doesn't mean you can't get dental coverage. You can simply buy a dental insurance policy. Delta Dental and Aetna offer them across the country, for example. You can also buy vision insurance. VSP is a major seller of this coverage. You can buy what's called Hospital Indemnity insurance which will cut you a check to help you pay your copays if you end up hospitalized. You don't have to get any of these within a Medicare Advantage plan; it might take a little digging, but they all exist on the open market. Or you don't need these at all. Just pay for your dental care out of your pocket. It's up to you.

Just because Medicare Advantage Plan A has $2,000 worth of dental allowance doesn't mean you should choose it if the MOOP is $7,550. Not when Medicare Advantage Plan B has $1,000 worth of dental with a MOOP of $4,000. It doesn't make financial sense (in my opinion). It also probably doesn't make financial sense to buy a $40 per month Medicare Advantage plan just because the extras are so rich when a $0 plan has all of your doctors in the network and has better prescription drug benefits than the $40 option.

Prioritize. That's what I'm asking you to do. What's most important? I'm glad you asked.

Repeating a line from a previous chapter, any insurance professional will tell you, at its core, an insurance product should provide financial protection for you, your family and heirs from catastrophic events. In other words, at a bare minimum, insurance should shield you from bankruptcy and financial ruin.

**Not having dental insurance won't cause you to go bankrupt. Not having vision insurance won't put you in the poor house. So, while the insurance companies and insurance agencies might market and highlight these extra benefits to get you to call them or click their ad, put it in perspective. They're nice to have; they're just not the most important.**

So, now what? Now, you must decide!

# CHAPTER SEVEN

# MEDICARE INSURANCE COVERAGE
## HOW TO PRIORITIZE

By this chapter, you have enough information to choose between Medicare insurance coverage Options 1 through 3. If not, now is the time! This chapter will help you prioritize your Medicare insurance coverage purchasing decisions.

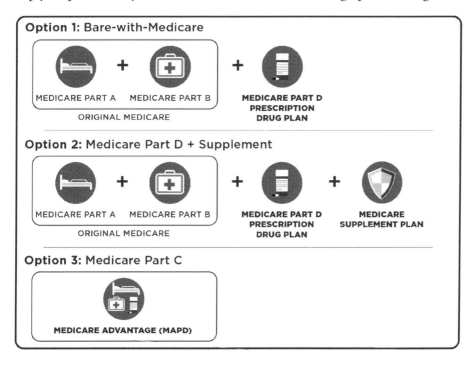

## OPTION 1: BARE-WITH-MEDICARE

In this scenario, all you're doing is keeping Original Medicare and buying one product—a Medicare Prescription Drug Plan from a Medicare insurance company. These are prioritized in order from most important to least important when you're buying a Medicare Part D Prescription Drug Plan.

**1** Are all of your prescription drugs on the formulary? In other words, are they covered? The answer needs to be a yes to move forward.

**2** Where do your prescription drugs fall within the formulary? Tier 1 drugs are the least expensive for you; Tier 4+ are the most expensive. The more prescriptions you have that fall into the Tier 1 or Tier 2 category, the better.

**3** Premium—the lower, the better.

**4** Yearly drug and premium cost—the lower, the better.

**5** Drug deducible—many companies have a deductible before any benefits kick in. Some only have deductibles on Tiers 3 and 4+. You optimally want to buy one with no deductible, but the yearly drug and premium cost is more important.

**6** Pharmacy—is your preferred pharmacy in the plan network? If not, and you don't have any particular allegiance to that pharmacy, are there others close by that you wouldn't mind using?

**7** Star rating—needs to be 3.5 or higher for the Medicare Part D Prescription Drug Plan.

## OPTION 2: ORIGINAL MEDICARE + MEDICARE PART D + SUPPLEMENT

MEDICARE PART A    MEDICARE PART B
ORIGINAL MEDICARE

MEDICARE PART D PRESCRIPTION DRUG PLAN

MEDICARE SUPPLEMENT PLAN

In this scenario, you're keeping Original Medicare and using the same process and prioritization as above to buy a Medicare Prescription Drug Plan. Next, you're also buying a Medicare Supplement plan on top of Original Medicare to fill in the coverage gaps. I'd recommend prioritizing your shopping and buying around the following items from most important to least important.

**1** Buy the most comprehensive Medicare Supplement plan you can. If you were eligible for Medicare before January 1, 2020, that's Plan F, followed by Plan C. If you weren't, those are no longer available. That means Plan G is the most comprehensive, followed by Plan N.

**2** Premium—the lower, the better. Don't be fooled by introductory rates—look at the premiums over time.

**3** Medicare star ratings don't apply to Medicare Supplement plans. Therefore, it's best to check the AM Best financial ratings of the Medicare Supplement companies you're considering (AM Best is a financial rating service). Most of the brand-name Medicare insurance companies you probably already recognize have high ratings, but if you're considering a smaller, lesser-known company, I'd check the ratings. You can do this by clicking on PrepareforMedicare.com/links and clicking the AM Best Consumer website link. Then, search under "Health & Accident" and click Medicare Supplement and your state.

## OPTION 3: MEDICARE PART C

In this scenario, you're buying a Medicare Advantage plan to cover your medical and prescription drug insurance needs. Remember, you can't have a Medicare Supplement or a Medicare Part D Prescription Drug Plan if you choose this option. Medicare Advantage plans supersede both.

By now, you've already read how incredibly complex these products can be, how different they are, and how many options you have available to you. You also know Medicare insurance companies and agencies will market to you by highlighting things like dental coverage, over-the-counter pharmacy allowances, eyewear allowances, and gym memberships. They do this because they know you like the idea of those things. However, recall that the first rule of insurance is to provide, at the very least, financial protection for you, your family and heirs from catastrophic events. In other words, insurance at a bare minimum should shield you from bankruptcy and financial ruin. The extra bells and whistles, such as having eyewear coverage, are fine as long as you have the big stuff covered first.

Here's how I recommend you narrow down your choices.

In all instances, **try hard to avoid any deductibles on the medical or the prescription drug benefits. Medicare insurance companies have been quietly introducing deductibles into Medicare Advantage plans over the last few years, but there are still plenty of options without deductibles available.** The lower the potential or actual costs, the better.

**1** Are your doctors in the insurance company's provider network? Is your preferred hospital in the insurance company's provider network? For doctors you see often, it's best to actually call their offices to double-check. If not, find a plan that has them in the network.

**2** Monthly premium—the lower, the better, but don't let a $0 plan premium automatically sway you.

**3** Primary care and specialist doctor copays—the lower, the better.

**4** Prescription drug coverage—Are all of your prescription drugs on the formulary? In other words, are they covered? The answer needs to be a yes to move forward.

**5** Where do your prescription drugs fall within the formulary? Tier 1 drugs are the least expensive for you, Tier 4+ are the most expensive. The more prescriptions you have that fall into the Tier 1 or Tier 2 category, the better.

**6** Prescription drug copays—the lower, the better.

**7** Avoid deductibles on prescription drug coverage. Many companies have a deductible before any benefits kick in. Some only have deductibles on Tiers 3 and 4. You optimally want to buy one with no deductible.

**8** MOOP—try to keep it under $4,000 per year.

**9** Avoid any deductibles on medical coverage.

**10** Inpatient hospitalization coverage—the lowest daily copays, for the fewest number of days is the best.

**11** Outpatient costs—try to find coverage at a fixed-dollar amount; avoid coinsurance if you can.

**12** Diagnostic procedure costs—Lab, X-rays, etc.

**13** "Extra" benefits (dental, vision, hearing, etc.). Dental allowance should be at least $1,000 per year.

**14** Star Rating needs to be 3.5 or higher.

Once you've answered the questions for your selected Option, frame and summarize them by using the Four C's.

## COST, COVERAGE, CHOICE, AND CONFIDENCE

As I've noted earlier in the book, there are plenty of Medicare Part D Prescription Drug Plans available to you across the country. The same goes for Medicare Supplements, but some states offer more options than others. **Medicare Advantage choices are typically plentiful in metro areas, fewer in suburban areas, and non-existent in some rural areas.**

Here's how you should frame your purchasing decisions.

- ✓ **COST**
  - ✓ What's my monthly premium?
  - ✓ How much will my prescription drugs cost?
  - ✓ How much will it cost me to go to the doctor or the hospital?
  - ✓ What's my MOOP?

- ✓ **COVERAGE**
  - ✓ Are my over-the-counter supplements, hearing aids, vision, and dental needs covered? Other extra benefits?
  - ✓ Do I get a free gym membership with the insurance policy?
  - ✓ Can I use my insurance plan benefits when I travel?

- ✓ **CHOICE**
  - ✓ Can I see my doctor(s)? How much will that cost me?
  - ✓ Can I see a large number of doctors? (Is the network large?)
  - ✓ Can I see any doctor that accepts Medicare?
  - ✓ Are my prescription drugs covered?

## ✓ CONFIDENCE

✓ Do I know the insurance company? Is it a brand I can trust?

In all cases, you're going to want to **be comfortable with the reputation and confident in the brand of the Medicare insurance company you're selecting or considering.** As you've seen throughout the book, there are only a handful of big-brand Medicare insurance companies that have hundreds of thousands of customers. That's not to say you have to buy from a big-brand Medicare insurance company, but I do urge you to do some research on their websites, ask friends, family, and Medicare insurance agents how they feel about their customer service and stability. You can also take them for a test drive. Call the companies you're considering and do some shopping. Ask questions. Did you wait on hold for a long time? Bad sign. Poke and prod the phone representative. Ask what plans are available and how they treat their customers. You can find out a lot just by talking with phone representatives.

Finally, all of these steps and prioritizations can be found on the website for easy reference if you'd like to head over there to print off a checklist PrepareforMedicare.com.

Now it's time to take action. It's time to buy Medicare insurance.

CHAPTER EIGHT

# HOW TO BUY MEDICARE INSURANCE
## USE AN AGENT

Now that you've (a) decided which path to take and (b) understand how to prioritize what's important for each path, it's time to begin the process of shopping for and purchasing a plan.

This section is for everyone—folks new to Medicare and folks who have been on Medicare for a while.

I can't stress this enough—if you're approaching retirement, you need to start this process *before* you turn sixty-five or retire. Over the course of my career, I've seen multiple studies that say a very small percentage of people start doing research to even understand what Medicare is, much less what Medicare path might be best for them, before age sixty-five. I get it; it's not everyone's favorite topic. However, don't be one of those people who put off the pain until the last minute and expect miracles to happen. My advice is to meet with an agent or begin the DIY process while you're still working and considering retiring, or while you're sixty-four, so you've got plenty of time to review your preferences and options.

If you've already been on Medicare for some time and have already chosen one of the three coverage options, remember you can switch Medicare Advantage plans and Medicare Part D Prescription Drug Plans once a year during the AEP. Don't forget about the OEP, either. Just because you already have a Medicare Part D Prescription Drug Plan and a Medicare Supplement doesn't mean you have to stay there for life. In fact, you need to shop around *every year* during the AEP to make sure you're in the right plan with the right company. You can switch your Medicare Advantage plan or your Medicare Part D Prescription Drug Plan during the AEP. You can switch your Medicare Supplement, too—just realize you'll most likely have to answer medical questions to qualify for a new plan. Some states have different rules (see Chapter Four).

Before you're ready for this next section, you're going to have to have made a choice, or at least prioritized one of your three Options for consuming your Medicare benefits.

Remember our three Options? Here they are again, and I've bolded what you'll have to purchase from a Medicare insurance company.

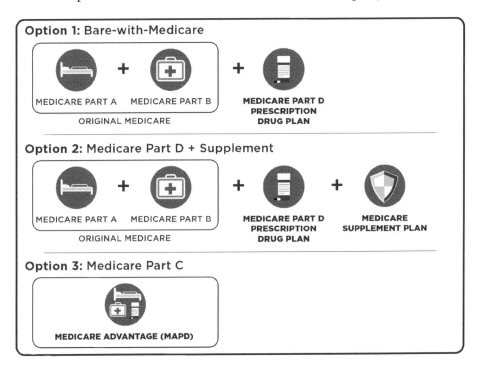

Okay, you're all set. You know which Medicare insurance path you want to walk down, or at least you have a general idea of what your preference is, even though you may be willing to consider another option.

You need to do a little preparation (Chapter Seven) before taking the next step of either talking to a Medicare insurance agent or beginning the DIY process yourself. **I'd recommend you write down the following information (and head to the website PrepareforMedicare.com for free checklists you can print and use):**

**1** Three options (Option 1, 2, or 3)

**2** Your enrollment period (AEP, OEP, IEP). Don't worry if you don't know this, but if you need a refresher, it's in Chapter Two.

**3** Write down your prescription drug names, how often you take them, and dosages. Or bring your prescription bottles with you if you're consulting with an agent.

**4** Write down any doctors you've seen in the past or plan to see over the next twelve months. Hospitals and facilities, too.

**5** If you're a snowbird or if you travel often, write down where you plan to visit.

**6** Details of the plan you're currently on, as well as what you like and don't like about it.

**7** Any additional benefits you would like, such as dental, vision, hearing, etc.

Again, you can find some handy checklists on the website at PrepareforMedicare.com.

Great! Now you're ready to begin.

What now? Now, you have to buy something.

How? Glad you asked. There are two ways, but first, you've got to decide what kind of Medicare Consumer you are. This question was posed at the very beginning of the book, remember? Let's review.

Are you Person #1?

⊘ I like to shop for the best deal. I like to research and know everything about a subject. I'm skeptical of salespeople, and I like to DIY everything..

Or, are you Person #2?

⊘ I don't like this whole process. I don't want to deal with it. Make it easy for me; do it for me or tell me how I can outsource this decision by using a Medicare insurance agent.

If you're Person #1, I'm going to show you how to DIY the whole buying process. That's coming up in the next chapter.

But first, we're going to address the solution for Person #2 because, quite frankly, that probably describes most of you reading this. If you're Person #2, you need the help and should outsource this process to a Medicare insurance agent.

## MEDICARE INSURANCE AGENTS

I've been using the term "Medicare insurance agents" throughout the book, and now you get to learn all about them. First of all, I use the phrase, "Medicare insurance agents," not because they work for the federal government, are specifically endorsed by the Centers for Medicare and Medicaid (CMS), or work directly for Medicare, the federal program. I use the phrase simply to separate them from, say, a Progressive or Liberty Mutual insurance agent who sells auto, home, and life insurance. I also use the phrase because insurance agents who specialize in health insurance don't, by default, also specialize in Medicare insurance. Medicare insurance agents, as we'll see, are special.

They're also hard to find. Telephonic agents are relatively easy if all you want to do is buy something over the phone. But finding a local Medicare insurance expert you'll want to have on your team can be difficult. I'm going to show you how to find one and how to make sure they *are* the expert agent you're looking for.

Let's also get this out of the way. All insurance agents—Medicare, auto, home, and life—get commissions of some sort for selling you a product. We'll explore whether or not those commissions influence what they sell you later in the chapter. The main point I want to drive home first is this; whether you buy a Medicare insurance policy directly from the insurance company or through an agent, *the price is the same.* **You save exactly zero dollars by buying the same product directly from the Medicare insurance company. Likewise, you can't get a cheaper rate or premium by buying a policy from a Medicare insurance agent.**

Using my two decades of experience interacting with and training thousands of health insurance agents across the country, I can confidently say that there are somewhere between 90,000 and 120,000 agents who specialize in Medicare across the US. While that might sound like a lot, when you stop and think about the fact that there are sixty-seven million people on Medicare, the quick math means that's only one agent for every 558 to 745 Medicare recipients.

To be an agent who specializes in Medicare, a person must first have a health insurance license issued by the state in which he or she lives. To get that license, prospective agents must go through general classroom or online training and pass a state-specific test before being issued a license. Once they have that license, they have to complete a number of Continuing Education (CE) credits before their license can be renewed in future years. This license is normally all they need to sell life or health insurance. However, selling Medicare insurance is very specialized and highly regulated. Just as Medicare insurance plans, premiums, and benefits change all the time, so do the rules that govern them.

Since Medicare is a federal program, there are federal rules to follow. States may have their own rules around Medicare Supplements, as those are largely state-regulated products, but Medicare Advantage and Medicare Part

D Prescription Drug Plans are regulated at the federal level. As such, Medicare publishes guidance material to insurance companies and agents outlining the specific requirements and rules they must follow to be allowed to sell insurance to the Medicare population.

Among them:

Agents must be licensed in every state they operate in and then sign contracts with insurance carriers to be able to sell their products. So, for example, if an agent wanted to sell Medicare insurance policies issued by United Healthcare, they'd have to fill out and send in a contract, pass a background check, and sometimes even submit to a credit check before they're approved and appointed by United Healthcare. They have to do this for every single carrier they wish to represent.

But they're not done yet.

Then, agents must be trained and tested annually by *each insurance company they represent and* pass the annual test with a score of at least 85%. The training takes hours to complete just for one company. That means if an agent wants to represent and sell Medicare products for Humana, United Healthcare, Aetna, and their local Blue Cross and Blue Shield plan, they have to take training at each company and pass four tests with at least an 85% score every year. Most Medicare insurance agents only do this for two to five companies, *which means not every agent can sell every product available to you.* Most tend to make sure they're able to sell products from the large national or regional insurance companies like Aetna, United Healthcare, Humana, Cigna, Blue Cross and Blue Shield, and Centene/WellCare. However, there are lots of smaller Medicare companies out there that some agents don't bother to get contracted and licensed to sell for. It's important for you to understand that **not every Medicare insurance agent sells products for every Medicare insurance company.**

As you can see, this is a very lengthy and tedious process for insurance agents to go through. To pass their tests every year, they can't just be a casual Medicare insurance agent. They have to be dedicated to Medicare recipients and love the work. This process tends to weed out those agents less dedicated to their craft and equips agents with very detailed ins-and-outs with regard to the complex Medicare insurance space.

As part of the training and testing, agents are expected to know all the enrollment periods, plan types and options, and be able to explain them to people in a way that's understandable. The training also reminds them of the lengthy and specific guidelines they must follow in order to not run afoul of federal rules and regulations. Yes, Virginia, Medicare insurance sales are highly regulated and for good reason. Medicare made these rules to protect people on Medicare from unscrupulous or pushy salespeople.

## MEDICARE INSURANCE AGENT CONSUMER PROTECTIONS

One of the big rules Medicare insurance companies and agents must follow involves asking personal health questions. If you're applying for a Medicare Advantage or a Medicare Part D Prescription Drug Plan, company representatives may *not* ask health questions. You can certainly volunteer them, and frankly, most people do because it usually helps the Medicare insurance agent determine the right plan for their particular situation. This doesn't hold true for Medicare Supplements, however. Why? Because Medicare is an entitlement program, and you're guaranteed acceptance into a Medicare Advantage plan and Medicare Part D Prescription Drug Plans regardless of your health status. They're considered part of the federal Original Medicare program, which also does not discriminate based on health status. Medicare Supplement plans and insurance companies technically fall outside of the federal Original Medicare program, as they're considered gap plans. That's why Medicare Supplement insurance companies are normally allowed to ask health questions outside of your Open Enrollment Period for Medicare Supplement plans.

Again, most people don't find this all that big a deal, but the point is, Medicare insurance companies and agents who sell Medicare Advantage and Medicare Part D Prescription Drug Plans aren't allowed to ask you about your health. It's understandably kind of hard for an agent to help you find the right Part D Prescription Drug Plan without knowing what prescription drugs you take, wouldn't you agree? That's why most people disclose some level of health and prescription drug information to their agents when interacting with them.

The only catch is the agent or insurance company representative can't ask you for it directly or *require* you to disclose it.

What are some of the other consumer protections around which Medicare has rules and regulations? Well, there are a lot, but I've pulled them together from the Medicare Communications and Marketing Guidelines and other sources, which are published and updated annually for insurance companies and agents. I've taken the liberty of wordsmithing them for you, so they're clearer. But, if you'd like some night-time reading, you can always head to the website PrepareforMedicare.com/links to read them yourself.

Insurance agents and insurance company representatives who are selling Medicare Advantage and Medicare Part D Prescription Drug Plans may *not*:

- ✓ Knock on your door unsolicited, canvas door-to-door, or leave sales information such as a leaflet or flyer at your home.

- ✓ Call you, unless you have an existing insurance policy with that insurance company or are the current client of that insurance agent.

- ✓ Approach you in public or a common area (e.g., parking lots, hallways, lobbies, sidewalks, etc.) and try to sell you something.

- ✓ Call you on the phone or text you to get you to buy something unless they already know you and have a pre-scheduled appointment with you.

- ✓ Call you about one product—say, life insurance or Medicare Supplement plans and then turn that conversation into a sales call for Medicare Advantage or Medicare Part D Prescription Drug Plans. This is known as a bait-and-switch tactic.

- ✓ Call a friend or family member of yours just because you said they might be interested in a Medicare insurance policy. If you want to give a referral to your insurance agent, your friend or family member will have to call your insurance agent.

⊘ Call former customers who have canceled their policy to get them to sign up for a new plan.

⊘ Call you if you attended a sales event or sales seminar unless you gave express consent or permission at the event or seminar to have the agent call you.

⊘ Market to you in a healthcare setting, such as a patient exam room, hospital patient rooms, treatment areas where patients interact with a healthcare provider and clinical team and receive treatment (including dialysis treatment facilities), and pharmacy counter areas (where patients interact with pharmacy providers and get medications).

Each insurance company is responsible for the behavior of the Medicare insurance agents who sell their products. Thus, each insurance company has its own agent monitoring, compliance, and oversight teams who look at reams of data, including customer service complaints, to monitor sales agents in near real-time. While rare, sometimes an agent breaks a rule or does something they're not supposed to. When it happens, insurance companies are swift in their investigations and, if necessary, punishment. This can range from documented counseling, up to and including contract termination. If it's egregious, an agent's infraction can be reported to the State Department of Insurance, in which case the agent can face the loss of his or her insurance license and be subject to hefty state and federal fines.

## THE THREE TYPES OF MEDICARE INSURANCE AGENTS

There are three types of Medicare insurance agents—field-based agents, hybrid phone and web-assisted agents, and Medicare insurance company call center agents. Some agents specialize in Medicare Advantage, while others specialize and prefer Medicare Supplements. Ideally, you want one that specializes in Medicare Advantage, Medicare Part D Prescription Drug Plans, *and* Medicare Supplements. It's important to ask when you interview them, as I explain later in this chapter.

# 1. FIELD-BASED AGENTS

These agents live in your local area and sell insurance by individually meeting with their potential and current customers. Often, they will come right to your house and review your options across the kitchen table. If you don't want them in your home, they'll meet you at a Starbucks, library, McDonald's—anywhere that's convenient for you. These appointments usually take an hour, sometimes longer, and sometimes require more than one sitting. Many agents have started doing meetings over Zoom or other videoconferencing as well.

The advantages of using a field-based agent are many. They usually know what Medicare insurance plans are available where you live, which companies are new, and which have been around for years. They know which companies are rolling out new and exciting plans, and which ones are on their way out of the area. These agents are normally hyper-connected to their local insurance company representatives and know what's going on with each company they represent.

They know which doctors and hospitals are in one company's network and not in others. They know which plan is hot that year and which plans are not. They know all of the particular state-based rules around Medicare Supplement insurance. They take pride in providing great customer support and service and often hand-hold their clients through many decisions.

Great field-based agents proactively reach out to you every fall to do an annual plan review with you to go over your existing coverage to see if it's still the right plan for you. They know when prescription drug formularies change, when prices go up, and when benefits go down. They make sure you get your ID cards when you buy a new policy. They're available via phone, almost 24/7. You might even get a birthday or holiday card from them. If you value having a local advocate helping you navigate the Medicare maze on your behalf, find a really good field-based agent. They can be invaluable.

There are two types of field-based Medicare insurance agents: Independent agents and Captive agents.

## Independent Insurance Agents

Independent agents are also known as multi-carrier agents, which, as the name suggests, are contracted to sell products for multiple Medicare insurance companies. They'll usually be able to sell a number of Medicare Supplement insurance companies, Medicare Part D Prescription Drug Plans, and Medicare Advantage plans. These agents usually work *with* an independent insurance agency, but not *for* an agency. It's a loose affiliation. In other words, the independent insurance agency doesn't technically employ the independent agent, but they may provide certain administrative services like contracting, customer service and scheduling help. In return, the independent agent aligns their Medicare insurance company contracts with the independent agency, and the agency also makes a small commission every time the agent makes a sale.

Most independent insurance agents only represent three to seven companies, which again, means that not every agent can sell every product available to you. Most tend to make sure they're able to sell products from the large national or regional insurance companies. However, there are lots of smaller Medicare insurance companies out there for which some agents don't bother to get contracted and licensed to sell. That doesn't mean they're not worthwhile to research; many of them offer fantastic products. It's again just important for you to understand that not every Medicare insurance agent sells products for every Medicare insurance company.

## Captive Insurance Agents

Captive agents normally work for a Medicare insurance company and may only sell that company's products. For example, Humana employs quite a large captive sales force, and those agents may not sell United Healthcare or Aetna Medicare insurance policies, only Humana's.

There are some hybrids of this model; some insurance agencies do employ captive agents, but those agents *are* allowed to sell products from more than one Medicare insurance company—just not whichever company they want or choose, like the independent insurance agent can.

## 2. HYBRID AGENTS: ONLINE INSURANCE AGENCIES

Hybrid insurance agents, who use a combination of the telephone assisted by comparison tools found on websites to sell Medicare insurance, are very quickly gaining in popularity. Companies like eHealth, SelectQuote, GoHealth, and many others employ thousands of insurance agents who can sell insurance over the phone. Some hybrid agencies have field-based agents as well. These companies are multi-carrier agencies, which means they sell people insurance policies from multiple Medicare insurance companies. These companies loosely fall under the emerging, Insurtech space which, in simple terms, utilizes real people on the telephone assisted by internet-based decision tools and even artificial intelligence to help people buy Medicare insurance policies. Many of these agents are seasonal as companies ramp up their hiring towards the end of the year to handle the influx of calls during the AEP. Once the AEP ends, they usually let those seasonal agents go and keep a core number of their best agents throughout the remainder of the year and into the following year. This process begins anew in the July and August timeframe to prepare for the next AEP.

You're not likely to get the same deep, first name basis relationship with your insurance agent if you buy a policy through one of these companies. These agents work in large call centers sprinkled throughout the country or work remotely out of home offices. You dial a toll-free number to talk to them, and, odds are, you'll get a different agent every time you call in. But that's just fine for a lot of people. Many people simply don't value, want, or need a local agent to hand-hold them through the process. They don't want an agent in their homes, sitting across from them at the kitchen table. They find these companies' websites very informative and helpful and, once they're done looking at their options and narrowing down their choices, they pick up the phone to speak with an agent to get a little 1-on-1 assistance.

Make no mistake; while hybrid agencies want you to initially engage with them via their websites, their real goal is to get you to call them on the phone. That's because they know they have a much better chance of selling you an insurance product over the phone than if you just use their website. They design their entire website around this concept. It's not a bad thing; it's just the way they do it. I'd estimate about 80% of their customers start researching insurance options on their websites, then pick up the phone to talk to an agent.

There's another component of hybrid insurance agencies that may give you pause. When you use them, some will ask for your email address and phone numbers upfront as part of the buying process. In other words, many of them ask you for contact information and permission to contact you even if you don't buy something from them. They try to capture this information from you upfront so they can market to you either via email or by calling you. Even if you buy something, many of them will reach out to you via email, mail, and phone to get you to buy something else from them. This is known as cross-selling. Did you buy a Medicare Supplement plan from a hybrid insurance agency? Odds are, they'll try to get you to buy a Medicare Part D Prescription Drug plan, too—or a homeowner's policy, or a "final expense burial" life insurance policy. Some agencies are very aggressive in their marketing, others aren't. Not every hybrid insurance agency does this, but a few do.

Personally, I don't like this. I understand why they do it (more money earned per customer and add-on sales), but I don't particularly like being marketed to unless I give someone express permission to do so. It's probably because I'm very sensitive about giving out my personal information unless I'm buying something, and I like the ability to opt out of providing the information at any time. That's not to say they're not providing valuable information; they are. But they're marketing to you, nonetheless.

I don't like unsolicited email in my inbox either. And I certainly don't like getting phone calls from a company I didn't buy anything from. So, just be aware of this and choose a hybrid insurance agency you're comfortable with. There are a good number of options in the back of this book to choose from.

One of the Frustrating Flaws in Chapter Three I noted was the many shortcomings of the Medicare.gov site. The websites these companies develop are amazing and very advanced when compared to Medicare.gov and even some insurance company websites. They display multiple products from multiple companies, which are customized by you simply entering in your ZIP code. Once you've done that, voila! All the Medicare insurance choices you could possibly need or want are right there on the screen in front of you. You can even enter in your prescription drugs and doctors (which Medicare.gov can't do) and sort by what you find important.

If you need help, there's a 1-800 number to call, and that's how you reach these types of insurance agents. If you don't need or want that interaction with an insurance agent, you can just buy your policy right there online without any assistance whatsoever.

**The best time to call any insurance company or agency is in the middle of the week, either early in the morning or after 4:00 p.m. That's because people generally get their mail between noon and 3:00 p.m. and then immediately pick up the phone to call. Avoid calling on Mondays—hold times on Mondays are the longest of any day of the week.**

## 3. INSURANCE COMPANY CALL CENTER AGENTS

Every Medicare insurance company either directly employs or contracts with third-party call centers to provide licensed insurance agents to take insurance applications over the phone. If you call a Medicare insurance company's toll-free number you found on a piece of mail you got in your mailbox, off of a TV ad, or a website, you'll be routed to these call centers.

Just like the hybrid agents working for online insurance agencies, companies begin to recruit and train seasonal agents towards the latter half of the year in preparation to handle the massive influx of phone calls during the AEP. When it's over, they also keep a core group of their best agents and let the rest go. This cycle repeats every year.

These agents are considered captive as well and, as they're working for or on behalf of the Medicare insurance company, are *not* multi-carrier. They can only sell insurance for the company they are representing, so when you call them, they can't show Medicare insurance options from other companies.

## SCOPE OF APPOINTMENT

When you engage any Medicare insurance agent, field-based, hybrid or telephonic, and begin talking about specific insurance plan benefits and premiums, every agent selling either Medicare Advantage plans or Medicare Part D Prescription Drug Plans is required by Medicare rules to first have you agree to what's called a Scope of Appointment. When this happens, or you're asked to agree to this, don't be alarmed; it's all part of the process. You're not signing up for anything; you're not making promises to buy a particular product, nor are you signing your life away. Some people get nervous when they're asked to sign insurance forms before even talking about buying a policy. It's understandable. They think they're buying something when, in reality, they're just giving another person permission to talk to them about Medicare insurance products.

Medicare doesn't have a standard Scope of Appointment that it mandates all Medicare insurance plans to use, so it leaves the creation of it up to the insurance carriers. However, when some folks remain skeptical or suspicious of filling this form out, it's natural for them to search Medicare.gov. When you do, it won't pop up. Medicare doesn't really address it anywhere online or in any of their guides that I can find. It's certainly not in the most recent "Medicare and You" guide published by Medicare. The requirement is only embedded in something called the Medicare Communications and Marketing Guidelines, which the general population doesn't use. Insurance agents and insurance companies use them; the general population does not.

So, when agents ask people to sign these, and clients type , "Scope of Appointment" into the Medicare.gov search box, noting useful is displayed. I don't know why.  Just know this: Medicare requires this process. **Some people are taken aback when an insurance agent says they need a Scope of Appointment. Don't be. It's all very normal. You're not buying anything. You're not disclosing personal or financial information. You are simply giving someone permission to talk to you about Medicare insurance policies.**

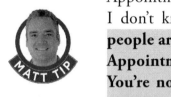

The Scope of Appointment is meant to be a consumer protection device. It's ostensibly required to ensure that folks on Medicare don't get pressured into buying something they don't want or don't need and have a clear understanding of what the agent is allowed and not allowed to talk to you about. In theory, this is in place so an insurance agent can't start pressuring you to talk about a Medicare Advantage plan if the only thing you want to talk about is a Medicare Supplement and a Medicare Part D Prescription Drug Plan.

The Scope of Appointment must be documented for all marketing activities, in-person and over the telephone—this means any time that you interact with a Medicare insurance agent in person or over the phone. It must be completed before any appointment where you're talking to an agent about buying Medicare insurance. It can be done on paper, over email, or on a recorded line.

Here's what needs to be captured:

- ✔ Product types to be discussed
  - ✔ Most companies and agents rightfully suggest agreeing to discuss "all" Medicare products up-front on the Scope of Appointment. If not, you'll have to fill out another one if you later decide you want to talk about other options.
- ✔ Date of appointment
- ✔ Your name, the agent's name, and contact information
- ✔ The form must state that there's no obligation to enroll, that current or future Medicare enrollment status will not be impacted, and that automatic enrollment will not occur.

## SCOPE OF APPOINTMENT NOT ALWAYS REQUIRED

The Scope of Appointment form is not required during sales and marketing seminars. So, if you get invited to and attend a seminar to listen to Medicare options and decide to buy a product at the end of the seminar, you won't need one.

Scope of Appointment forms often differ from one health insurance plan to another. The form usually indicates the sales agent does not work for the federal government and may benefit from the sale of the health product, which means they will get a commission for the sale.

The forms also bear the notice that signing the appointment form is not a binding agreement to enroll in any plan. The form does not affect your current or future enrollment status in any Medicare plan.

Medicare rules and regulations require that all Medicare insurance agents secure a Scope of Appointment to proceed with most appointments, either over the phone or in-person, unless you or someone on your behalf has physically, telephonically, or electronically signed and submitted the form to the Medicare insurance agent. They must keep a record of this on file for at least ten years.

## HOW DO I FIND A FIELD-BASED AGENT? HOW DO I FIND A HYBRID OR TELEPHONIC-BASED AGENT?

Finding insurance company telephone agents is pretty easy. For example, if you want to talk to a Humana call center Medicare insurance agent, just go to Humana's Medicare website and call the number on the screen. That'll pop you right into a sales call center. Remember, if you're calling a Medicare insurance company, they're going to route you to telephone Medicare insurance agents who *only* sell you that company's product. I list a number of Medicare insurance company websites on my website, and you can find them here: PrepareforMedicare.com/links.

The same goes for the hybrid agent. All you have to do is go to their website and call the first toll-free number you see. That'll take you right to a Medicare insurance agent. Since you're calling a Medicare insurance *agency*, and not a Medicare insurance *company*, you'll get a phone rep who can sell Medicare insurance products from multiple companies. If you want to do it that way, head over to PrepareforMedicare.com/links for links to the large or popular hybrid agencies in this space. When you click through, their toll-free numbers are plastered all over their websites.

## HOW DO I FIND A FIELD-BASED AGENT NEAR ME?

Most people *prefer* using a field-based agent who lives in their area. That said, finding a field-based agent is more difficult—but not impossible. There's no comprehensive database or website listing all of the agents that I know of (maybe someday I'll build that feature into the website). The Yellow Pages went the way of the dinosaur, and Googling this will flood your computer screen with a billion ads. To top it off, some field-based agents purport to sell Medicare insurance, but only sell Medicare Supplement insurance. **Ideally, you want an insurance agent who can sell all three products—Medicare Supplements, Medicare Prescription Drug Plans, and Medicare Advantage plans.**

As I mentioned earlier in the chapter, field-based Medicare insurance agents are a rare breed due to the relatively low numbers of agents specializing in Medicare insurance across the country. I'd also guess that out of the 90,000-120,000 licensed, trained, certified, and appointed Medicare insurance agent pool, more than a third of them are telephonic agents, which means field-based agents are even rarer.

So, how do you get in touch with a field-based agent? The easiest thing to do is ask friends and family for referrals. Who have they used? Did they have a good experience, or was it merely okay? Remember, even if you get a referral, the insurance agent isn't allowed to call you due to federal Medicare rules. *You* have to call *them*.

Another way of going about finding a field-based agent is to **call a big-name insurance company and ask *them* to send you an agent.** Since almost all Medicare insurance companies use independent or captive field-based agents to sell their products, they know who they are. Just pick one—United Healthcare, Aetna, or Humana, for example—and call the toll-free number on their website. Again, you can find a list of the websites on PrepareforMedicare.com/links.

When a telephone representative answers, tell them you're interested in their products but want them to connect you with a *local agent* in your area. In fact, you want to specifically ask them to have them connect you with *a local, independent agent* in your area. If you don't, they may send you a captive agent who can only sell that company's products.

Let's say you call Humana to do this. If you're 110% sure you want to buy a Humana product, then it doesn't matter if they send you a captive agent or an independent agent.

If you're *not* 110% convinced that you want to buy a Humana product, *then you want to specifically request an independent agent.* **I'd personally recommend you always specifically ask the insurance company to send**

**you an independent agent.** That way, you know the independent agent can sell you a product from that company, but because they're independent, they can also sell you products from other Medicare insurance companies.

So, when the phone rep picks up the phone, say something like this. *"Hello! I'm interested in learning more about your products, but I'd like to talk to a local independent agent in my area. Can you help me?"*

When this happens, the telephone representative may attempt to lead you down a path to buy something from them over the phone. Or they may want to mail or email you marketing material or an application. Don't let them take you down that path; just repeat yourself. Something like, "That sounds great, but I won't be buying anything today and would like to talk to a local *independent* agent in my area."

What the representative should do from there is capture some basic information from you— where you live, your phone number, and the type of plan(s) you're interested in. Then, the telephone representative will probably record the Scope of Appointment, so you'll want to at least anticipate that.

If you want to set up an appointment for an agent to come to your house, you can typically do that right then on the phone with the insurance company representative. Many Medicare insurance companies will press you to set a time, date, and location so the Medicare insurance agent can just come to your house. They do this because they know you're more likely to buy something if they can get an agent inside your house, sitting at your kitchen table.

**However, I'd recommend you don't set up a home visit just yet.** Instead, I'd ask them to *note you'd like the Medicare insurance agent to simply call you first.* That's because you need to know a little bit more about your agent before you take the next step of setting up an appointment in your home. Specifically, you want to make sure you're being introduced to an *expert* Medicare insurance agent.

## HOW DO YOU KNOW YOU'VE GOT AN *EXPERT* LOCAL FIELD-BASED AGENT?

Once you connect with an independent Medicare insurance agent, you'll want to interview them. This applies to any field-based agent, independent or captive. You won't be able to do this for telephone agents.

Wait, what?

Yep. You need to ask your potential Medicare insurance agent-for-life some very specific questions to make sure they are a person you'll want to keep on your team. A good agent can sell you an insurance policy. A *great* agent, an *expert*, is what you're looking for here. You should be looking for a Medicare insurance agent you can trust and rely on for a very long time because, ideally, he or she is helping you review your coverage annually and helping you with any customer service problems throughout the year when they arise.

As I've already covered, Medicare insurance agents are a rare breed, but that doesn't mean 100% of them are *experts*. Just like everything in life, only a small percentage of Medicare insurance agents are top-notch experts in their field. Your goal is to find one of these great agents. You want to find a low-pressure, consultive salesperson who educates you and guides you through your needs, and helps you find the right fit. You're looking to weed out the high-pressure, move-fast salesperson who just wants to get in and get out of the appointment with a sale.

This is why, when the agent calls you, you call them, or the agent shows up in-person (only if you've invited them, of course), have some questions ready. My advice is to do this over the phone before setting up an in-person appointment. **You may want to interview more than one agent until you find one who answers your questions to your satisfaction.**

Remember, it's important to find a top-notch, experienced, knowledgeable, super-professional Medicare insurance agent you can count on for life.

Here are some questions you should ask your potential agent over the phone before scheduling any next steps or in-person appointments. You can head over to PrepareforMedicare.com to print out helpful checklists, too.

Are you ready? Okay, here's your Walter Cronkite moment!

**1** How long have you been a Medicare insurance agent? (Needs to be over three years.)

**2** Do you consider yourself a full-time Medicare insurance agent? (Needs to be a yes.)

**3** Do you sell Medicare Advantage plans as well as Medicare Supplement plans? (Needs to be yes.)

**4** How many companies do you represent? (Needs to be a minimum of three, including a smattering of the big national ones—United Healthcare, Humana, Aetna, and Mutual of Omaha, for example.)

**5** Which Medicare insurance company products do you sell the most of and why? (Should be a good smattering of Medicare Supplements, Medicare Advantage plans, Medicare Part D Prescription Drug Plans, and some dental, vision, or other ancillary insurance products.)

**6** How many customers do you currently have? (Needs to be over 100.)

**7** Of those customers, how many are Medicare Advantage customers, and how many are Medicare Supplement and Medicare Part D Prescription Drug Plan customers? (Needs to be a nice balance.)

**8** How many complaints from customers to the insurance company or Medicare have you been asked to respond to by the insurance company in the last twenty-four months? (Needs to be zero.)

**9** Walk me through how you treat your customers when they buy a policy from you. (Needs to explain what they do immediately after you buy a policy, as well as when and how they review your coverage—should be at least once a year.)

**10** How much commission do you make when you sell me a policy? (Needs to be specific and without much hesitation. Every expert agent knows *exactly* how much commission he or she makes per sale. Didn't you know your salary while you were working? Of course you did. They may pause when you ask, because not many people actually ask them this question! That's okay. But if they refuse to tell you or deflect, watch out and move on.)

That last question about commissions is going to be a touchy topic, probably for both you and your insurance agent. However, it's an important question to ask because the answer is going to give you some valuable insight into the psyche, professionalism, and forthrightness of your potential Medicare agent-for-life.

A professional, expert Medicare insurance agent won't have any issue at all telling you how much commission he or she stands to make when selling you a product. If an agent balks, then move on. Remember, independent Medicare insurance agents are just that—*independent*. That means they're independent contractors with no base salary, no benefits, no car allowance, and no gas money. They pay taxes on those commissions. Just like all of us, we work (or worked) and expect to receive compensation for our time, effort, expertise, and experience. The same holds true for independent Medicare insurance agents. The difference is, unlike a salaried employee, they only make money when they sell a policy. That money is paid to them by the Medicare insurance company, not you. That means *until you buy something from them, they're essentially working pro bono—for free.*

Ask them how much commission they're making if you enroll in the product they're selling. If they say they don't know or refuse to tell you, end the conversation right then and there. If your independent Medicare insurance agent won't disclose their commissions to you, what else are they not telling you?

**In my opinion, you *want* a successful, highly paid Medicare insurance agent in your corner. You *want* them to be well-dressed and drive a premium automobile to your appointment or meeting. You *want* them to be proud to tell you how much commission they make. You *want* them to have hundreds of happy customers who have previously bought Medicare insurance with their help. You *want* them to be really, really good at what they do. After all, do you want to be associated with a poorly paid, poorly dressed, financially *unsuccessful* Medicare insurance agent as your agent-for-life? Not me!**

If the insurance agent answers all of these questions to your satisfaction, now's the time to move ahead and set up a face-to-face sales appointment. Typically, this means the agent will come to your house or meet you at some other location, but it can also mean a Zoom meeting or other web-based videoconference. The meeting can also happen right over the phone. These meetings normally last anywhere between forty-five minutes to two hours, depending on the complexity of the Medicare insurance issues you're both trying to solve together.

If the insurance company didn't originally have you agree to a Scope of Appointment, the agent will do this now or in person when you meet.

Once you reach this stage—meeting with a Medicare insurance agent—it's generally time to buy something. That's what the insurance agent will expect you to do, and that's what you've prepared for! Sometimes it'll take a couple of meetings to get comfortable with the products and with each other. At the very least, you'll have a broader understanding of your options. You can always schedule a follow-up appointment if you need more time to think about it before you purchase a policy.

## HOW DO INSURANCE AGENTS GET PAID?

First of all, any compensation—be it commissions, salaries, or bonuses paid as a result of a Medicare insurance policy sale—is not directly paid by you, the Medicare consumer. Nor does agent compensation directly influence the price or monthly premium you'll pay. Your premium does not go up or down if you buy a policy from an independent Medicare insurance agent or captive agent, online or over the phone. The price you'll pay for a Medicare Advantage plan, Medicare Supplement, or Medicare Part D Prescription Drug Plan is the same no matter where or how you buy it.

Speaking from decades of experience with Medicare insurance agents, commissions rarely, if ever, influence professional Medicare insurance agents. 99.9% of Medicare insurance agents are fine, upstanding, moral, high-character people who *always* put the best interests of their customers first. If they're not, they will soon be found out and stripped of their insurance license. But like any industry (financial planning, stock market, etc.), there are always a few bad apples who don't do the right thing and, more often than not, end up on the evening news. (You can see an example of this at PrepareforMedicare.com/sources).

As we've already seen, Medicare insurance agents selling Medicare products go to great lengths to remain compliant with Medicare regulations and laws. They must be licensed as an agent, which means sitting through hours of classes for each company they represent to remain certified to sell every single year. They must also take continuing education classes every year to keep their insurance license. Insurance companies have an extremely low tolerance for agents who do not follow the rules and are quick to terminate their ability to sell their products if they suspect any improprieties.

So (very good) odds are, the Medicare insurance agent you're dealing with for your Medicare insurance needs is highly trained, ethical, honest, and a highly regulated sales professional who knows the business, knows the local market, and knows what plans are (usually) the best for you.

That said, the compensation paid in the form of commissions, bonuses, or incentives to Medicare insurance agents does vary.

## DO COMMISSIONS INFLUENCE MEDICARE INSURANCE AGENTS?

It's one of the biggest questions many people silently ask themselves—how do I know if my Medicare insurance agent has my best interests in mind and is not influenced by earning the highest possible commissions for themselves when enrolling me in a Medicare plan? Is my insurance agent selling the policy that best fits my needs, or simply selling me a product that pays him or her as much as possible?

## INDEPENDENT MEDICARE AGENT COMMISSIONS

Independent Medicare insurance agents selling Medicare Advantage and Medicare Part D Prescription Drug Plans receive commissions when they sell a policy. These commissions are the same for every single Medicare insurance company. That's because Medicare regulates the maximum commission amount that a Medicare insurance company can pay anyone selling a Medicare Advantage or Medicare Part D Prescription Drug Plan.

Over a decade ago, these commissions were not regulated, and that led to different insurance companies offering some staggeringly high commissions for selling Medicare Advantage plans—at times as high as $850 or more per sale. That led to a number of folks complaining to Medicare that their agents were inappropriately placing them into plans based upon those high commissions and not because it was the best plan for them.

That all changed around 2007 when Medicare stepped in and mandated that Medicare insurance companies pay the same commission amounts and imposed steep penalties for not doing so. Now, Medicare insurance companies selling Medicare Advantage and Medicare Part D Prescription Drug Plans are limited to a maximum commission amount that they're allowed to pay Medicare insurance agents for policy sales. Medicare insurance companies are not required to pay the maximum commission rate. Most pay the maximum, but not all do. Now that they're standardized, it's hard to argue that there's any real financial incentive for Medicare insurance agents to inappropriately steer you to one plan over another or to switch your coverage every year. On top of the highly regulated nature of the Medicare insurance arena, coupled with the Medicare insurance company's monitoring and oversight of their Medicare insurance agents, there's just simply no real financial reason for a Medicare insurance agent to inappropriately switch your coverage every year or favor one Medicare Advantage plan or Medicare Part D Prescription Drug Plan over the other.

## CURRENT MEDICARE-MANDATED MEDICARE ADVANTAGE AND MEDICARE PART D PRESCRIPTION DRUG PLAN COMMISSION RATES

For plans that go into effect in 2022, Medicare allows Medicare insurance companies to pay Medicare insurance agents a maximum of $573.00 for the first year of the policy, and $287.00 every year after that. The $573.00 is paid if you've recently enrolled in or qualified for Medicare for the first time or are buying a Medicare Advantage plan for the very first time. If your agent is merely switching you from one Medicare Advantage plan to another Medicare Advantage plan, they are only eligible to receive the renewal rate of $287.00. These are annual amounts, and they change every year. In CT, PA, NJ, DC, and CA, those amounts are higher. The amounts are lower in Puerto Rico and the US Virgin Islands.

For Medicare Prescription Drug Plans, that commission amount is $87 for the first year and $44 in the following years. The same logic applies as found in the Medicare Advantage commissions scenario above; it's hard to argue that an insurance agent has an incentive to enroll you in one Medicare Part D Prescription Drug Plan over another because they make the same commission amount regardless.

## MEDICARE SUPPLEMENT COMMISSIONS

The issue of commissions gets a little murky when talking about Medicare Supplements. Unlike Medicare Advantage and Medicare Part D Prescription Drug Plans, Medicare Supplements are mostly regulated by the states, not the federal government. Unlike Medicare Advantage and Part D plans, commissions are not the same for each company, and the plans they offer can vary quite a bit. These commissions are paid as a percentage of the Medicare Supplement's premiums. For example, Company A might pay 15% sales commission for year one, and 10% commission for years two through six. Company B might pay 22% sales commission for year one and 15% commission for years two through ten. If one company pays more than the other for the same Medicare supplement insurance policy, are you sure your agent is putting you in the product that best fits your needs and budget? Let me remind you, 99.9% of the time, that answer is a resounding *yes*. But how do you know? Ask questions.

## BUYING A MEDICARE SUPPLEMENT PLAN? ASK QUESTIONS IF YOUR MEDICARE INSURANCE AGENT ONLY SHOWS YOU POLICIES FROM ONE MEDICARE INSURANCE COMPANY.

As we've seen, most independent Medicare insurance agents represent multiple Medicare insurance companies. It's almost impossible for them to have contracts with all Medicare insurance companies. So, if your agent only presents you with one Medicare Supplement option, ask questions. Ask them, "Why this option from this particular Medicare insurance company and not others?" After all, remember the medical benefits for Medicare Supplement plans G, F, N, and all other letter-based Medicare Supplement plans are the same, regardless of the company logo. Be active, inquisitive, and vocal; challenge them! There's usually a good reason that is totally unrelated to the commission they stand to make. In many cases, your agent may be recommending that you take one option over another due to lower premiums, fewer medical questions on the applications, or because of certain discounts offered from that particular Medicare Supplement insurance company that others don't offer. **The key here is to *ask*. Ask them *why* they think this is the best plan for you.**

## HOW DO HYBRID OR TELEPHONIC-BASED AGENTS GET PAID?

Generally, the same commissions I listed above are paid out for Medicare insurance policy sales by a hybrid or telephonic Medicare insurance agent. The only difference is if those agents are *employed by* insurance call centers, agencies, or companies. In other words, if they *aren't* independent contractors, their employers will give them a percentage of those commissions and not the whole amount.

## OKAY, I HAVE AN APPOINTMENT WITH A MEDICARE INSURANCE AGENT SET UP. HOW DOES THIS ALL WORK? WHAT'S THE PROCESS?

1. Agent shows up at your home or location of your choosing. This can also be done over the phone or via Zoom, etc.

2. You fill out a Scope of Appointment if you haven't done so already.

3. You provide the agent items from your checklist (found at PrepareforMedicare.com).

4. You and the agent begin discussing your needs, eligibility to buy a policy, enrollment windows, and plan details.

5. You decide to enroll in a plan, or you arrange a follow-up appointment.

During all sales appointments; in-person, on the phone, or otherwise; Medicare insurance agents are allowed to:

**1** Discuss various plan options with you.

**2** Distribute plan materials, including the enrollment kit for the insurance product.

**3** Distribute or collect enrollment forms.

**4** Advise on how to get plan information (for example, through the mail, a website, or customer service); and

**5** Provide educational content.

However, the sales agent cannot market non-healthcare-related products until at least forty-eight hours after the original appointment. In other words, this goes back to the bait and switch provisions in the Medicare regulations and guidelines—agents are forbidden to talk about anything other than what's on the Scope of Appointment without asking permission or filling out a new Scope of Appointment. They can't pivot into selling you a life or auto insurance policy, or an annuity during a Medicare appointment.

During the sales process, expect great Medicare insurance agents to ask a lot of questions. This is a good thing! They're trying to understand your needs and help you find the plan that is most suitable for you.

**Sample questions a Medicare insurance agent might ask you:**

✔ Are you eligible for Medicare?

✔ Are you still working?

✔ Have you retired?

✔ Are you currently on Medicare?

- ✔ What kind of insurance coverage do you have?

- ✔ What do you like about it? What don't you like?

- ✔ Which Medicare option are you considering?

- ✔ What doctors do you use, and are they important to you?

- ✔ Would you be willing to switch doctors?

- ✔ What hospitals would you prefer to use if you need to?

- ✔ Is prescription drug coverage important to you?

- ✔ Are there any upcoming appointments or health care services you think you'll need in the next year or so?

- ✔ Do you travel?

- ✔ Do you have dental insurance?

- ✔ Do you go to the gym?

- ✔ What can you afford in terms of a monthly premium?

- ✔ Does anyone else need to be a part of this process?

Hopefully, you've thought about these and have those answers ready using your checklist.

**Ask questions and listen. Use your checklists and write down the answers. If it makes sense to buy a product right then and there, go ahead. If not, ask to set up a follow-up appointment, then buy a product. It's that simple.**

# CHAPTER NINE

# HOW TO BUY
# MEDICARE INSURANCE
## DIY (DO IT YOURSELF)

Well, hello there, Medicare DIY consumer Person #1! This is your section. Remember, you're a Medicare consumer that likes to shop for the best deal by doing research and knowing everything about a subject. You're skeptical of salespeople and like to DIY everything.

Sound familiar? If you don't want to use a Medicare insurance agent, are willing to take a bit more time, and are perfectly happy and content to do this all online all by yourself, this is the section for you!

Just as there are three Medicare paths, there are three DIY options to choose from. You can use one of the three DIY options for all three Medicare paths, but I'm going to recommend you use different DIY options for each of the three Medicare paths. Here they are again:

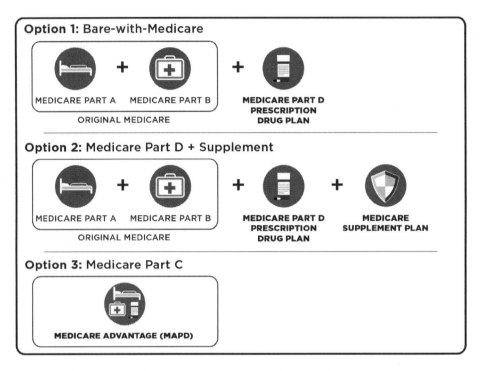

First of all, you need to have a general idea of the path you want to take before you move to this stage. It will be very helpful to have filled out the same checklists you would have done had you decided to use a Medicare insurance agent. I think we've all sat down at a computer screen to do research only to get pulled into Alice in Wonderland's rabbit hole and emerge three hours later wondering where the time went and what happened. As I've previously mentioned, online internet marketers are very good at getting you to click their ads, hyperlinks, and more and more web pages. They're working very hard to get you to call them or click something. Resist the temptation. Keep your checklist(s) by your side and follow the DIY prescription below.

Keep in mind, these steps are constantly changing. I'll update these steps on the website when I can, but even if they change a bit, you still should generally be able to get where you intended to go.

## MEDICARE.GOV

Medicare.gov is the most-used website for people researching Medicare coverage. It makes sense; it's a government website, so there's no sales spin and no flashy graphics or marketing messages. It displays all of the options available to you, and you can research and click around to your heart's content without feeling pressured.

Yet, as I've already covered in Chapter Three, there are a number of what I call "Frustrating Flaws" with this website. Yes, it certainly lists all of the product options available to you, and you can enroll in Medicare Advantage and Medicare Part D Prescription Drug Plans right through the website. But the Medicare Supplement section is barely even what I'd consider helpful. The overall website navigation is difficult. Entering your location, prescriptions, and preferred pharmacies is easy enough, but it's useless when looking for doctors while researching Medicare Advantage plans. Medicare.gov doesn't even house Medicare Advantage network data; to look that up, you have to go to different websites. To top it off, when you enter in sorting and filtering parameters, the data isn't sorted in ways that make it user-friendly. In short, it's a government website and outclassed by a slew of Medicare insurance company and insurance agency websites.

That's not to say you shouldn't use it. You should, but my advice is to **only use it for two purposes: buying a Medicare Part D Prescription Drug Plan and narrowing down your Medicare Advantage choices.**

## OPTION 1: BARE-WITH-MEDICARE

Here, I'd recommend using Medicare.gov exclusively to buy your Medicare Part D Prescription Drug Plan. In fact, **Medicare.gov is a fantastic place to do this—probably even better, faster, and more convenient than using a Medicare insurance agent.** It can be done in under an hour if you've got all of your pre-work checklists at the ready.

Just a quick refresher; if you choose this option, all you're doing is using Original Medicare to cover your medical healthcare and buying a Medicare Part D Prescription Drug Plan. The DIY process for buying a Medicare Part D Prescription Drug Plan through Medicare.gov is pretty easy.

Here's how to do it, step-by-step:

**1** Navigate to Medicare.gov in your web browser.

**2** Click "Find Health and Drug Plans."

**3** Click "Continue Without Logging In."

&#10004; You can create an account or log in if you already have one, but it isn't necessary.

**4** Click the third option, "Drug Plan (Part D)."

**5** Enter your ZIP code when prompted. Validate the county you live in if asked.

**6** Click the last option, "I don't get help from any of these programs," then click Next.

**7** Click yes when asked, "Do you want to see your drug costs when you compare plans?"

**8** Click one of the three options that apply to you when asked, "How do you normally fill your prescriptions?" I would suggest using monthly as the option for viewing ease. Click Next.

**9** In the next section, "Add prescription drug," enter in all of your prescriptions, including dosages and frequency. Reference your worksheet if you've filled it out.

**10** When you're done adding in all of your prescriptions, click "Done Adding Drugs."

**11** The next screen asks you to find your pharmacy. Search for your preferred pharmacy by name—or there's a helpful map on the page to use. You can enter up to five, but I'm guessing you probably only use one. Click "Done" at the lower right-hand part of the page when you're finished entering data.

What pops up are all of your Medicare Part D Prescription Drug Plan options. The screen will default to being sorted by "Lowest Drug + Premium Cost." That's a good way to sort your results. If you want to find plans without deductibles, you can do that by clicking the drop-down in the upper-right corner of the screen and selecting "Lowest yearly drug deductible." If you simply want to sort by the lowest monthly premium, you can do that too.

Whichever of the three sorting mechanisms you choose, I'd focus on the top three results. Give them a quick glance to make sure each of them is rated three and a half stars or above; I'd recommend you never consider anything under three stars. If the plan is flagged "Plan too new to be measured," that's okay, but realize it's a brand-new Medicare Part D Prescription Drug Plan.

The next step can be as simple or as complicated as you want to make it. You can compare up to three Medicare Part D Prescription Drug Plans side-by-side. Or you can just pick the top result and roll with it.

Either way, when you're ready to enroll, you just click, "Enroll." This will take you to a screen where you'll have to confirm your enrollment period. If you need a refresher, reference your checklist or workbook, or go back to Chapter Two and confirm that you're using the right enrollment period.

Once you've chosen your election period, click "Next."

This starts a seven-step process.

**Step 1 of 7:** Enter your Medicare number, which can be found on your red, white, and blue Medicare card. Click "I've read and understand the contents of this page," and click Next.

**Step 2 of 7:** Fill out your name, DOB, gender, and phone number. Make sure your name is the same as what's on your Medicare card. Click Next.

**Step 3 of 7:** Enter your primary home address. Click Next.

**Step 4 of 7:** The next section asks several questions about any other drug coverage you have, whether or not you work, and whether or not you want your Medicare insurance plan documents physically mailed to you or just sent to your email. When you're done filling this section out, click Next.

**Step 5 of 7:** This section asks if you want to have the monthly premiums deducted from your Social Security or Railroad Retirement Board (RRB) benefits. You can choose this one (the easiest option, in my opinion), or you can elect to pay your plan directly. Be forewarned, sometimes it takes several months for Medicare, the Medicare insurance company, and Social Security to catch up and synchronize the billing. If you don't want that potential hassle, select Auto Bill Pay.

**Step 6 of 7:** This section is the legalese asking you to confirm what you've previously entered. Fill it out and click Next.

**Step 7 of 7:** This is the confirmation screen.

You're done! You've just signed up for a Medicare Part D Prescription Drug Plan.

## WHAT HAPPENS NEXT?

You'll receive your Medicare Part D Prescription Drug Plan card in the mail generally within two weeks. You'll also get information in the mail unless you elected to receive plan documents via email. If you've messed anything up in the application process, the Medicare insurance company will reach out to you. It's important that you respond to them as quickly as possible.

## OPTION 2: ORIGINAL MEDICARE +
## MEDICARE PART D PRESCRIPTION DRUG PLAN +
## MEDICARE SUPPLEMENT

I'd recommend using Medicare.gov exclusively to buy your Medicare Part D Prescription Drug Plan and then use a Hybrid Agency website to buy your Medicare Supplement plan.

Just a quick reminder: if you choose this option, you're using Original Medicare to cover your medical healthcare, adding a Medicare Supplement plan, and buying a Medicare Part D Prescription Drug Plan. There are two steps to this process.

**Step 1:** Follow the DIY process previously outlined to buy your Medicare Part D Prescription Drug Plan.

**Step 2:** Follow the DIY process below to buy your Medicare Supplement plan.

You can buy a Medicare Supplement plan on any number of the Hybrid Agencies I list on the website at PrepareforMedicare.com/links. However, as of this writing, many of those websites only let you get a step or two into the research before asking you for either more personal information or trying to get you to call their toll-free number. The only one I can find (as of this writing) that allows you to shop multiple plan options and companies side-by-side online without being prompted to talk to a phone rep is eHealth. If you're a DIY-er, you want to shop for Medicare Supplement plans by yourself and *not necessarily* talk to a phone agent.

I'm not specifically recommending eHealth. They've just been around for decades and sell a whole lot of insurance policies. I'm not recommending any specific Hybrid Agency. But I can't possibly walk you through more than one website experience and keep this chapter under a million words. Feel free to use any hybrid agency you want—it doesn't matter to me. Each of them uses a similar process to what I've outlined below, but there will be slight variances. Many hybrid agencies ask you for your email address and phone number upfront, but some do not. I don't like entering my email or phone number anywhere I don't have to, because I don't want them to call me or email me. But I'm probably a bit over the top with this concern. As far as I can tell, eHealth does not do this.

Whichever hybrid agency you use, you want to make sure you're on their Medicare Supplement section, not their Medicare Advantage or Medicare Part D Prescription Drug Plan section.

Why am I recommending using a hybrid agency website to do this? Well, first of all, I've already outlined why Medicare.gov is essentially useless for Medicare Supplement research and enrollment in Chapter Three. Another reason is that **this saves you the hassle of going to each Medicare Supplement insurance company website one by one. The hybrid agency websites rank, sort, and filter these for you. Most, if not all, of these hybrid agency websites have the large Medicare Supplement companies on their platforms. Many hybrid agencies also have many of the smaller, less well-known Medicare Supplement insurance companies listed, too, if you want to check those out.** Finally, even though you're buying this DIY style online, you're still buying this through an insurance agency. That means you may get communications and outreach from the agency.

Here's how to do it, step-by-step:

1. Enter www.ehealthinsurance.com into your internet web browser.

2. Right there on the home page, it'll have a drop-down menu to continue shopping for Medicare. If it doesn't, move the drop-down to Medicare and click "Continue Shopping."

3. On the next page, enter your ZIP code and click "Shop Plans."

**4** Once you've done that, the next page will default to showing you *only* Medicare Advantage plans. Click the "Medicare Supplement Insurance Plans" towards the top of the page.

**5** This page will default to sorting by "Promoted Plans" on the right-hand side of the page. Click that drop-down box and sort by "Monthly Premium."

**6** On the very first result, click "View Price." It doesn't matter what kind of plan or company it is at this stage. Don't worry. You're not enrolling when you do this. This is how you get the website to prompt you for your birthday and Medicare Parts A and B eligibility dates, which you'll need to have when you eventually *do* apply for a policy.

**7** When you click "View Price" in the previous step, a pop-up will show up and ask you to enter your birthday, gender, and tobacco status. Fill this out and validate that your ZIP code is correct.

**8** When you enter your birthday, the website will automatically fill out what it *thinks* your Medicare Parts A and B eligibility dates are. Validate those dates by comparing them to your red, white, and blue Medicare card. If the website has them wrong, change them here.

**9** When you hit Next or Submit, the website will take you back to the page that shows you the Medicare Supplement options available in your area. Only this time, they've adjusted the rankings and the prices based upon your age. Stop and make sure they're still sorted by "Monthly Premium."

**10** On the left of the page, under the Filter Plans by column, click the check box on only the Medicare insurance companies you want to see.

**11** Then, just under that on the left-hand side of the page, under Plan Type, select Plan G. If you've already decided to consider Plan N, or any other plan, here's where you select those too. However, I'd stick with looking at only one type of plan at a time because it can get confusing.

Give it one last glance to make sure they're still sorted by "Monthly Premium." Now, you're able to see all Plan G options offered by the Medicare insurance companies you selected. From there, you can compare plans side-by-side by clicking on "Add to compare list." Or you can just click the lowest-priced Plan G and move forward.

If you want to move forward with buying a plan, click the "Enroll Now" button on the plan you want to buy. This will start the application process. There are five steps to this process.

> **Step 1 of 5—Applicant:** Add your name, address, height, weight, phone number, and email address. Some companies ask for more information; some companies ask for less. Click Next.
>
> Enter your Medicare number, which can be found on your red, white, and blue Medicare card. Validate that that your Medicare Parts A and Part B effective dates are correct. Click Next.
>
> **Step 2 of 5—Coverage:** This page will take you through various eligibility questions. Answer all of them, and then click Next.
>
> **Step 3 of 5—Additional:** This section will ask for any additional information the Medicare insurance company might need. It might also ask if you're eligible for any of their discounts, such as household discounts. Fill it out and click Next.
>
> **Step 4 of 5—Payment:** Yep, you guessed it. Here's where you say how often you want to pay your premiums and how you want to pay them. Fill this out. Click Next.

**Step 5 of 5—Summary:** This last page summarizes all of the information you previously filled out. Now's the time to validate it all. Click "Continue." This will take you to an Agreement and Signature page. Check the required boxes and electronically sign the application. Click "I Agree" to submit your application. You've just purchased a Medicare Supplement plan.

## WHAT HAPPENS NEXT?

You'll get confirmation letters or emails confirming receipt of your application. You will also get a follow-up call from the insurance company if they need to validate any information you provided on the application.

Expect to get your ID cards in the mail within fourteen days. Since you bought the policy through a hybrid agency, you may also receive follow-up correspondence from the agency; in this case, eHealth.

There's a second DIY option for this—and that's (again) buying your Medicare Part D Prescription Drug Plan on Medicare.gov and then buying your Medicare Supplement plan directly from the Medicare insurance companies. As previously noted, the big names in Medicare Supplement insurance are Mutual of Omaha, Humana, United Healthcare (AARP co-branded), CVS Health/Aetna, and various Blue Cross and Blue Shield plans. The only issue with this approach is—you guessed it—you have to go on each of their websites to compare prices and plans individually. You can do it, but it will take hours and hours of your time. At that rate, you'd probably be better off overriding your DIY tendencies and simply calling an independent Medicare insurance agent.

## OPTION 3: MEDICARE ADVANTAGE (MAPD)

Here you have two DIY options to choose from when buying a Medicare Advantage plan. For the first DIY option, you can use Medicare.gov to narrow down your top three choices, then move over to the Medicare insurance company websites to finish your research and buy the policy. For the second DIY option, you can use a hybrid agency website to buy your Medicare Advantage plan.

Just a quick reminder: if you choose this option, you're using a Medicare Advantage plan with Medicare Part D benefits embedded into the plan. This is also known as an MAPD plan and covers your medical and prescription drug coverage.

## OPTION 3: VERSION 1
### Medicare.gov + Medicare insurance company websites.

This version will have you hopping between a few different websites before actually making your purchase. Be sure to have checklists (found on the Prepare for Medicare website) filled out and ready to go. If not, at least have your prescription drugs and your doctors written down and handy.

The steps I'm outlining are many; this is going to be a very labor-intensive project and will probably take you an hour or two from start to finish. This is due to one of the Frustrating Flaws on the Medicare.gov website; you can't look up which providers are in and out of network. So, what we're going to do is use Medicare.gov to narrow down your choices, *then* move over to the Medicare insurance company's website to look up doctors and enroll. Let's go!

Here's how to do it, step-by-step.

**1** Navigate to Medicare.gov in your web browser.

**2** Click "Find Health and Drug Plans."

**3** Click "Continue Without Logging In."

  ✅ You can create an account or log in if you already have one, but it isn't necessary

**4** Click the second option, "Medicare Advantage plan."

**5** Enter your ZIP code. Click "continue."

**6** A question will pop up asking, "Do you get help with your costs from one of these programs?" Click the last one, "I don't get help from any of these programs."

**7** A question will pop up asking, "Do you want to see your drug costs when you compare plans?" Click yes.

**8** A question will then pop up asking, "How do you normally fill your prescriptions?" Select any of the three options that apply to you. Click Next.

**9** In the next section, "Add prescription drugs," enter in all of your prescriptions, including dosages and frequency. Reference your worksheet if you've filled it out.

**10** When you're done adding all of your prescriptions, click "Done Adding Drugs."

**11** The next screen asks you to find your Pharmacy. Search for yours by name, or there's a helpful map on the page to use. You can enter up to five, but I'm guessing you only use one. Click "Done" at the lower right-hand part of the page when you're finished.

The Medicare Advantage plans available in your area will pop up. They will display in the default sort order— "Lowest drug + Premium cost."

Before we move on, let's do a quick review.

Earlier in the book, **I recommended that you prioritize buying a Medicare Advantage plan using the following considerations, from most important to least important.** Here's the list again:

1. Are your doctors in the insurance company's provider network? Is your preferred hospital in the insurance company's provider network? For doctors you see often, it's best to actually call their offices to double-check. If not, find a plan that has them in the network.

2. Monthly premium—the lower, the better, but don't let a $0 plan premium automatically sway you.

3. Primary care and specialist doctor copays—the lower, the better.

4. Prescription drug coverage—Are all of your prescription drugs on the formulary? In other words, are they covered? The answer needs to be a yes to move forward.

5. Where do your prescription drugs fall within the formulary? Tier 1 drugs are the least expensive for you, while Tier 4+ are the most expensive. The more prescriptions you have that fall into the Tier 1 or Tier 2 category, the better.

6. Prescription drug copays—the lower, the better.

7. Avoid deductibles on prescription drug coverage. Many companies have a deductible before any benefits kick in. Some only have deductibles on Tiers 3 and 4. You optimally want to buy one with no deductible.

8. MOOP—try to keep it under $4,000 per year.

**9** Avoid deductibles on medical coverage.

**10** Inpatient hospitalization coverage—the lowest daily copays for the fewest number of days is the best.

**11** Outpatient costs—try to find coverage at a fixed-dollar amount; avoid coinsurance if you can.

**12** Diagnostic procedure costs—try to find coverage at a fixed-dollar amount; avoid coinsurance if you can.

**13** "Extra" benefits (dental, vision, hearing, etc.). Dental allowance should be at least $1,000 per year.

**14** Star rating—needs to be 3.5 or higher.

So, now you're on the default screen, which shows all of the Medicare Advantage plans available in your area. They will display the plans defaulted by being sorted according to Lowest drug + Premium cost.

Now it's time to use that list in concert with the filter and sort options on Medicare.gov.

## FILTER

At this stage, go to the filter option, which is located on the upper right-hand portion of the screen. It will open a pop-up screen. Click on the drop-down entitled, "Drug Coverage Options" and make sure you select "Includes Drug Coverage." Then, if you like PPO plans or HMO plans, you can filter your results by clicking either one. If you don't care, click both options.

While you're on the Filter tab, click Star Ratings and select "3 stars and up."

If you want to click on other items important to you on the Filter page pop-up, go ahead. When you're done, hit the "Apply" button. The pop-up window will close, and your plans will show up filtered by your preferences.

Now, take a look at your results. You can change the order of the sorting (remember, it defaults to Lowest drug + premium cost) by using that drop-down menu on the upper right. There are four options to choose from—"Lowest yearly drug deductible," "Lowest health plan deductible," "Lowest monthly premium," and the aforementioned "Lowest drug + premium cost."

## SORT

First, sort by "Lowest monthly premium." Then look at the first Medicare Advantage plan option that pops up. It'll show you the premium, Medicare's guess at how much your yearly drug and premium costs could be, the health deductible, and the drug deductible. It will also show you the MOOP. Great!

See that button towards the bottom of the page that says, "Add to compare?" You're going to use that.

Find the first option with the lowest monthly premium, with no deductibles on medical or prescription drugs and a MOOP at or under $4,000. If none of your options have those, pick the one with the lowest MOOP and lowest deductible amounts. Make sure it's a brand you're familiar with and click "Add to compare."

Do that for two more plans, for a total of three. No more than three, but two is okay.

When you've done that, you'll see your selections on the bottom of the page in a separate ribbon. When you're done, hit the "Compare" button.

You'll get a pop-up of all options displayed side-by-side.

Here's where you come in. Feel free to review all of the details of each plan to see how they line up with recommendations above.

Now comes the tough part, and the only way you can remedy Medicare.gov's Frustrating Flaw of not listing in-network providers on their website. This is how you satisfy recommendation number eight. Sure, you could click the "Enroll" button right now to start the purchasing process, but you will likely want to make sure your doctor(s) are in the network. Medicare.gov can't do this step for you. You have to do the legwork. Have a list of your doctors at the ready. You can also print off and fill out a checklist from the website PrepareforMedicare.com to help guide you through.

Now, pick the first plan option you think you'd like to explore and click "Plan Details."

Once the new webpage pops up, scroll down to the bottom. There you'll see a hyperlink to another website, labeled "View Plan website." Click that. That will open a new tab in your internet browser and take you to the Medicare insurance company's website. Then, find the link somewhere on the web page that says, "Find a Doctor." *Do not close the Medicare.gov website tab.* You're going back to that tab.

For this example, let's suppose we were researching a Humana plan. If so, when you clicked "View Plan Website," you'd have landed on their website at www.humana.com/medicare. Once the Medicare insurance company's website pops up, you need to locate the "Find a Doctor" option or "Find a Provider" option. On Humana's website, you'd have to scroll to the footer at the bottom to find it. There are so many Medicare insurance website versions out there, and each one is slightly different. Additionally, each website will probably default to a screen where they want you to enter your ZIP code, starting this process all over again, but *only* for their products. Don't do that—go to the "Find a Doctor" or "Find a Provider" option and click the link.

That's where you're going to search for your doctors, hospitals, or other healthcare providers. Make sure all of the doctors and hospitals that are important to you are listed in the network. If you're researching a PPO or an HMO-POS, remember those types of plans will allow you to see out-of-network doctors, but you'll most likely pay more to do so and may have to jump through some administrative hoops. Don't worry about searching for pharmacies—you already did that on Medicare.gov.

Once you've verified that your doctors are in your selected plan, go back to the Medicare.gov page you were on. Scroll back up to the top of the page and click "Go back to plan comparison." This will take you back to the two or three plans you were comparing.

Repeat this process for all two or three of the plans you're comparing, but remember, don't close the Medicare.gov website tab, or you'll lose your place.

Once you've found the plan(s) that have your doctors, you can click "Enroll."

When you do that, be ready (with the help of your checklist) with the following information:

- ✅ Your Medicare number (found on your red, white, and blue Medicare card).

- ✅ Information about your other health coverage (if you have any), including policy and group numbers (found on your health insurance card).

- ✅ Dates for when changes happened, like if you moved to a new address. This is your election period information.

Whew! Yes, this is a rather lengthy process, with many steps. I'm not telling you what to do here, but this is exactly why most people buy a Medicare Advantage plan with the assistance of a Medicare insurance agent. Or use …

## OPTION 3: VERSION 2
### Hybrid Agency websites

This version involves using a hybrid agency website to look up, research, and enroll you in a Medicare Advantage plan. Again, be sure to have your checklists by your side as reference guides. At the very least, you're going to need your lists of prescription drugs and your doctors handy.

Why am I recommending using a hybrid agency website to do this? I've already outlined why Medicare.gov is not a great tool for buying a Medicare Advantage plan DIY-style, but it boils down to this: Medicare.gov can't search for in-network doctors. Using a hybrid agency saves you the hassle of DIY Option #3, Version 1. **It cuts out the use of Medicare.gov *and* having to navigate each individual Medicare insurance company website. It's just easier and faster.** The hybrid agency websites rank, sort, and filter all of your Medicare Advantage options for you *and allow you to search for your providers all on one website.*

The steps for this process are fewer than the prior option, Version 1, and should take you about an hour. A word of caution: because this is essentially an online insurance agency, each agency must be contracted with Medicare Advantage insurance companies to be able to display them on their websites and sell them to you. This means that, unlike Medicare.gov, they probably don't show all of the Medicare Advantage plans available in your area. This is especially true in large metropolitan areas, which typically have many smaller or regional Medicare Advantage plans available, but for whatever reason, the hybrid agency doesn't have a contract with them to sell their Medicare Advantage plans. Finally, even though you're buying this DIY-style online, you're still buying this through an insurance agency. That means you may get communications and outreach from the agency. Ready? Let's go!

To buy your Medicare Advantage plan, head to any of the hybrid agency companies I list in the back of the book and type the address into your web browser. For simplicity, I'm going to walk you through the process as listed on the ehealthinsurance.com website, but it's similar for all other hybrid agencies. Again, I'm not specifically recommending eHealth. I'm just using them for this example because their user interface is very good for folks who like to DIY shop and compare. Each hybrid agency uses a similar process, but there will be slight variances.

Essentially, you want to make sure you're on their Medicare Advantage section, not their life insurance, car insurance, Medicare Supplement, or Medicare Part D Prescription Drug Plan sections. If you directly type the address in as I've listed it in the back of the book, it should take you right to the Medicare section.

## HERE'S HOW TO DO IT, STEP-BY-STEP:

1. Enter www.ehealthinsurance.com into your internet web browser.

2. Right there on the home page, it'll have a drop-down menu to continue shopping for Medicare. If it doesn't, move the drop-down to Medicare and click "Continue Shopping."

**3** On the next page, enter your ZIP code and click, "Shop Plans."

**4** Once you've done that, the next page will default to showing you *only* Medicare Advantage plans. Stay on that tab.

**5** This page will default to sorting by "Monthly Premiums" on the right-hand side of the page. That's good.

**6** On the left-hand side of the page, there are two links available where you can add your prescription drugs and your doctors. You're going to use both of those.

**7** Click "Add Rx Drugs." A screen will pop up where you'll enter your prescriptions. When you're done, there will be a link to "Add pharmacy" at the bottom of that pop-up window. Click that. Search for and add your preferred pharmacy. When you're done with that, click "See Plans."

**8** Now, click on the "Add your doctors" tab. Search for and add your doctors by last name. When you're done, click "See Plans."

**9** You'll find yourself back on the list of plans page, but this time they're sorted by Doctor Coverage. If you look at the first Medicare Advantage option, you *should* see green checkmarks beside the doctors you loaded if they're in that plan's network.

**10** Now, look to the left of the screen. Here's how you can filter your results. You can filter by company, monthly premium, or HMO or PPO plan type.

**11** What you can't do is filter by MOOP, whether the plans come with medical or prescription drug deductibles, or many of the other items you need to look at listed previously.

**12** When you're done filtering and sorting based on your particular requirements, take the top three results and click the checkbox in "Compare" for the first three plans. When you've done so, click the "Compare Now" button.

**13** That will take you to a screen that will show you information: star ratings, medical or prescription drug deductibles, your MOOP (ehealthinsurance calls it "out-of-pocket maximum"), doctor copays, inpatient hospitalization copays, etc. There's a lot of information. Compare the information to your checklist or workbook to make a choice.

**14** If you don't like any of the three options, go back and change your sort or filter options. If you like one and are ready to enroll, click the Enroll button.

**15** That will take you to a screen called "The enrollment process." Have your checklist and be ready to provide your Medicare ID number. Click "Start Secure Application."

**Step 1 of 3—Applicant Info:** This is where you enter all of your personal information. Fill it all out. Some items are optional—they ask you for permission to contact you for marketing purposes. Feel free to answer no—or yes. Up to you.

When you're done, click the "Next: Eligibility button."

**Step 2 of 3—Eligibility:** Enter your Medicare number, found on your red, white, and blue Medicare card. Then, fill out your Medicare Parts A and B effective dates. You'll have to also fill out some eligibility questions (refer to Chapter Two if you need to). You should already have the answers on your checklist or in your workbook. If there are supplemental benefits offered, you'll be able to buy those on this page. Also, there will be a drop-down (optional) for "How to Pay." I'd check the "Social Security Deduction." When you're done, click "Next: Review and Submit."

**Step 3 of 3—Review and Submit:** This is the last step. Review the information you provided, check the appropriate "Relationship to Applicant" box, and read and acknowledge the disclosures. When you're all done, click "Submit."

## WHAT HAPPENS NEXT?

That's it! You're all done! Well, almost. If you've done everything correctly, you can expect your ID cards and other plan documents in the mail. If you messed something up on the application, expect the insurance agency to reach out to you. Or expect the Medicare insurance company to reach out to you.

**Buying a Medicare Part D Prescription Drug Plan on Medicare.gov by yourself is pretty darn easy. (It's the easiest the DIY gets.) Buying a Medicare Supplement online is probably the next easiest because there are fewer offerings. Buying a Medicare Advantage plan gets *insanely* complex and difficult without expert advice.**

If you decide to DIY, fantastic! But know that the vast majority of people end up asking for professional help in making this decision and enrolling in Medicare insurance plans. **If you're feeling overwhelmed or unsure, engaging an expert Medicare insurance professional is most likely the best move and one I wholeheartedly encourage you to consider.**

## CHAPTER TEN

# ANNUAL MEDICARE "HOUSEKEEPING"

Like clockwork, every year around September and until the middle of December, Medicare insurance companies and insurance agencies will blast you with advertising. This is because the AEP runs from October 15 through December 7 every year. Remember—the AEP is the time where every single one of over sixty-seven million people on Medicare can change their Medicare Advantage and Medicare Part D Prescription Drug Plans. The advertising ramps right back up in January and continues through the end of the OEP, which runs from January 1 to March 31, every year.

Yet, recent studies show that more than half of those on Medicare don't shop their coverage once they get it. That is, many people on Medicare find it difficult to compare plans, are unaware of the open enrollment period, or are not confident in their ability to select a better plan. (Sources: PrepareforMedicare.com/sources).

What this means is that more than 50% of the people on Medicare bought a policy and then did nothing—they didn't or rarely shopped for a better deal—ever.

This is crazy. It's probably costing them real money, potentially thousands of dollars a year. **If you're not shopping every year, it's probably costing *you* real money!**

But realistically, I know that if your doctors, hospitals, prescription drugs, and prices haven't changed, you're likely to skip this. Over 50% of you can't all be wrong. It's a pain. It's confusing. It's scary. There are too many options. No one wants to mess their insurance coverage up. Plus, it's easy to let your Medicare Advantage plan or Medicare Part D Prescription Drug Plan just roll over into the new year. I get it. So, if this is you, you don't need to do anything during the AEP. If your Medicare insurance plan renews its contract with Medicare to provide your Medicare Advantage plan or your Part D Prescription Drug Plan for the following year, they'll renew you automatically.

That is exactly what Medicare insurance companies, Medicare insurance agents, and agencies want, by the way. They don't want you to shop every year. They don't want you to compare plans annually and potentially select a plan that better suits your healthcare needs. Why? Well, it costs insurance companies a lot of money to acquire you as a customer in the first place, and, in most cases, they have to pay a Medicare insurance agent a commission for the sale. Oftentimes, those costs eat up all the profit for the first year. Medicare insurance agents and agencies don't make a penny more in commission if you switch from one Part D Prescription Drug Plan to another every year. The same goes for Medicare Advantage plans—to them, it's just more work for the same commission.

We already know that premiums, benefits, deductibles, drug formularies, and doctor networks all change every year, without fail. New plans are offered, and old ones are taken away. It's also extremely likely your Medicare Advantage MOOP has gone up significantly in that time frame, so your maximum annual medical financial exposure is higher than it needs to be.

Even if you're on Option 2: Original Medicare + Medicare Part D Prescription Drug + Medicare Supplement plan and don't want or need to shop your Medicare Supplement every year (which is completely understandable), you still have to take a look at your Medicare Part D Prescription Drug Plan every year.

Lucky for you, dear reader, you're not in that group. You're now a part of the 50% of folks on Medicare who *do* shop their plans every year. If you're not, well—welcome to the club. You'll be ready to tackle this after reading this chapter.

## 1. USE YOUR AGENT

If you're working with a field-based Medicare insurance agent, a good one will do this every year for you. They may not actively shop plans for you, but they will proactively look at any of the changes and call you to review them on or after October 1 every year.

If you're using an agent and never hear from them, odds are, you don't have a good one. Lazy agents don't want to re-work your policy because they don't stand to make an additional commission. Find a new one. **Great—*expert*—Medicare agents review your policy every single year.** I show you how to find a fantastic Medicare insurance agent in Chapter Eight, so go back and re-read that if you need to find one.

If you've used a hybrid agency, call them and ask them to review the plan changes for you and offer recommendations. If you've used a Medicare insurance company's telephone agent, you can call them, too. But they're not going to give you any options other than the ones that particular company sells.

## 2. DIY

If you don't have an agent, don't want an agent, and prefer doing everything yourself, that's completely fine as well. Here's how to do it.

## READ YOUR ANNUAL NOTICE OF CHANGE (ANOC).

The ANOC is where (and when) Medicare insurance companies announce changes in the upcoming year for your Medicare Part D Prescription Drug Plan or Medicare Advantage plan coverage.

Every year, Medicare insurance companies change their Medicare insurance plans. Even if you stay on the plan you had the previous year, your benefits change regardless. Again, I've never seen a Medicare Advantage plan that *did not* change at least *something* from one year to the next. The same goes for Medicare Part D Prescription Drug Plans. Almost every plan makes some changes for the new year, so the costs and benefits in place on December 31 may be very different on January 1. Some of those changes can throw you for a loop if you're not aware of them or you're not prepared.

Here are some examples of what some folks get surprised with on January 1 every year.

**Surprise!** You might have a premium!

If you had a $0 Medicare Advantage premium, that may have changed. Every year, thousands of people get surprised in this way, all because they do not read their ANOC and only realize this when they either get a bill or notice a new deduction from their Social Security checks in January or February.

*But wait, there's more!*

**Surprise!** Your premium may be going up!

**Surprise!** Your prescription drugs are no longer covered!

**Surprise!** Your doctors are no longer in-network!

**Surprise!** You now have deductibles to pay!

**Surprise!** You no longer have dental coverage embedded in your Medicare Advantage plan!

No one likes those kinds of surprises. So, don't get surprised.

## YOU MUST READ YOUR MEDICARE ANOC (ANNUAL NOTICE OF CHANGE)

Not only is this title the most boring subtitle I've ever typed, but reviewing Medicare insurance company paperwork is also the most boring thing you'll do all year. However, think of it as what you'll have to do to save money. **If you follow my advice, it shouldn't take more than twenty minutes.**

By September 30 of each year, your Medicare insurance company is required to send you an ANOC. As the title implies, it outlines the changes to your plan for the following year. They usually give you *fifteen days to review what's in it* before the AEP begins on October 15. If you don't read your ANOC before then, you won't know what changes are being made to your plan until they go into effect on January 1.

The ANOC will usually arrive in your mailbox in a large, intimidating package with your insurance company logo affixed in the upper left-hand corner. Some companies send it to you via email. Please resist the temptation to throw this in the recycling bin or stash it near the phone in the "I'll-get-to-it-later pile."

I'm not even asking you to read the whole thing, just the important parts. What are the important parts? Immediately go to the section entitled, **_Summary of Important Costs_**. It should be right up front, either page two or three. This section will give you a brief overview of what the Medicare insurance company considers *important*. It's good as a summary, but *you might have to dig a bit deeper into the document to see everything that's going on.*

For Medicare Part D Prescription Drug Plans, here's what to check (in this order):

**1** Monthly premium. Did it go up?

**2** Did any prescription drug deductibles get introduced or increase?

**3** Check the formulary—did any prescription drugs you take get taken off the formulary or get bumped into a different (more expensive) tier?

**4** Check your prescription drug copays. Did they get more expensive?

**5** Scan it for anything announcing that the pharmacy networks have changed—did they drop your preferred neighborhood pharmacy?

**If *any* of the answers to those five questions are *yes*, it's time to shop.** Head to Chapters Eight and Nine to start shopping. You can use a Medicare insurance agent or DIY. Remember—just because you're shopping doesn't mean you're buying anything. Think of it as window shopping. If you see a better option, buy it. If not, keep what you have.

For Medicare Advantage plans, here's what to check (in this order):

**1** Monthly plan premium. Did it go up?

**2** MOOP—Did it go up or get worse? Is it over $4,000 per year?

**3** Doctor's office visit costs. Did the copays go up significantly?

**4** Inpatient hospital stay costs. Did they go up substantially?

**5** Did the potential costs for outpatient procedures go up?

**6** Part B Drugs—did the benefits get worse?

**7** Did any prescription drug deductibles get introduced or increase?

**8** Check the formulary—did any prescription drugs you take get taken off of the formulary or get bumped into a different (more expensive) tier?

**9** Check your prescription drug copays. Did they get more expensive?

**10** Scan it for anything announcing the pharmacy networks have changed—did they drop your preferred neighborhood pharmacy?

**11** Look for changes to your additional benefits, like dental, vision, and hearing. Any major? Any negative changes?

You may have to dig deeper into the document, beyond the ***Summary of Important Costs***, to find the good stuff. Scan the section entitled, *Changes to Benefits and Costs for Medical Services* as well as the *Changes to Prescription Drug Costs*.

Did anything change? *Of course* it did! These things change every year. At least now you know what's changing and what's not.

Since there are so many categories, you have to consider their costs. I'd stick to the following: **if the answer to 50% of those questions I listed here is yes, then it's time to shop. The exception to this rule is the MOOP. If the MOOP rose significantly or went over $4,000 a year, it's time to shop.** Head back to Chapters Eight and Nine to start shopping and, remember, you can DIY or find a good Medicare insurance agent to assist you.

## OTHER ANNUAL MEDICARE HOUSEKEEPING ITEMS

**1** **Wellness Exams**

If you're on Medicare, you get a yearly wellness exam. Don't forget to schedule this! The earlier in the year, the better. This is not only important for your general health, but it will also help make your overall healthcare run more smoothly. You can get a yearly wellness visit once every twelve months to develop or update what's called a *personalized prevention plan* to help prevent disease and disability, based on your current health and risk factors. Your provider may also perform a cognitive impairment assessment. This is all supposed to get you into your doctor's office at least once a year to check things out.

During this visit, your provider will ask you to fill out a questionnaire called a *Health Risk Assessment*. Answering these questions can help you, and your provider, develop this personalized prevention plan to help you stay healthy and get the most out of your visit. It can also include:

**a.** A review of your medical and family history

**b.** Developing or updating a list of current providers and prescriptions

**c.** Height, weight, blood pressure, and other routine measurements

**d.** Detection of cognitive impairment

**e.** Personalized health advice

**f.** A list of risk factors and treatment options for you

**g.** A screening schedule (like a checklist) for appropriate preventive services. Get details about coverage for screenings, shots, and other preventive services.

**h.** Advance care planning

Annual Physical Exams and Annual Wellness Exams are both covered by Medicare and are slightly different. **The best approach is to ask your physician to do "both" at the same visit.** They'll collect health information and work with you to develop a *"care plan"* for the year. If you have medical conditions that require a specific care plan, they may update that plan several times throughout the year as you achieve goals or make progress towards managing your conditions.

If you happen to have a Medicare Advantage plan that requires referrals for specialist visits like an HMO, you might be able to get anticipated referrals taken care of at this initial appointment with your primary care provider. **For instance, if you know you need to see your cardiologist at least two times a year, get those referrals while you're already in your PCP's office.** You can also find out what preventive care services and screenings you should take advantage of for the year. Medicare covers the following screenings along with many others: prostate cancer, colorectal cancer, mammograms, depression, diabetes—the list goes on. Getting into the habit of scheduling these Medicare Housekeeping peace-of-mind tests at the beginning of the year will help you make sure that it doesn't slip your mind.

### ❷ Authorization Forms

If you are brand new to Medicare or have never taken care of this in the past, you might want to consider filling out an Authorization Form to allow family or friends to call Medicare on your behalf. You must give prior permission in writing for someone to be given access to your personal health information. You can "revoke permission" or change the individual listed as authorized at a later date if you like. It's just important to make sure you take care of this before it's needed. Find the authorization form by hitting the website at PrepareforMedicare.com/links.

If you're helping mom or dad or another person enroll in a Medicare insurance plan online, over the phone, or via a paper enrollment application, each Medicare insurance company will ask you whether or not you're the legal representative or are otherwise legally able to act on behalf of that person. Medicare has a section in their regulations and guidelines that all Medicare insurance companies must follow, and here's a sample of what it says:

A Medicare beneficiary is generally the only individual who may execute a valid election for enrollment in or disenrollment from an MA (Medicare Advantage) plan. However, another individual could be the legal representative or appropriate party to execute an election form if a court has designated that individual as the proper party to take such an action on behalf of the Medicare beneficiary. The CMS will recognize State laws that authorize persons to effect an election for Medicare beneficiaries. Persons authorized under State law may be court-appointed legal guardians or persons having durable power of attorney for health care decisions, provided they have authority to act for the beneficiary in this capacity.

If a Medicare beneficiary is unable to sign an enrollment form or disenrollment request or complete an enrollment mechanism due to reasons such as physical limitations or illiteracy, State law would again govern whether another individual may execute the election on behalf of the beneficiary. Usually, a court-appointed guardian is authorized to act on the beneficiary's behalf. If there is uncertainty regarding whether another person may sign for a beneficiary, MA organizations should check State laws regarding the authority of persons to sign for and make health care treatment decisions for other persons. Where MA organizations are aware that an individual has a representative payee designated by SSA (Social Security Administration) to handle the individual's finances, MA organizations should contact the representative payee to

> determine his/her legal relationship to the individual, and to ascertain whether he/she is the appropriate person, under State law, to execute the enrollment or disenrollment. Representative payee status alone is not sufficient to enroll or disenroll a Medicare beneficiary.
>
> When someone other than the Medicare beneficiary completes an enrollment election or disenrollment request, he or she must attest to having the authority under State law to do so and confirm that a copy of the proof of court-appointed legal guardian, durable power of attorney, or proof of other authorization required by State law that empowers the individual to effect an election on behalf of the applicant is available and can be provided upon request to the MA organization or CMS.

(Sources: PrepareforMedicare.com/sources).

So, **if you're going to enroll a family member or someone else in a Medicare Advantage or a Medicare Part D Prescription Drug Plan, you're going to have to attest that you have the legal authority to do so under the state laws that apply.** And when you do, Medicare or the Medicare insurance company may ask you at some point to prove that, if it ever comes into question.

### ❸ MyMedicare.gov

My Medicare.gov is a convenient tool for folks using Option 1: Bare-with-Medicare or Option 2. By signing up, you are given access to a convenient, online service that puts your personal Medicare information at your fingertips anytime, day or night. After you sign up, you can begin using the site's services by completing an *Initial Enrollment Questionnaire* that will ensure your bills are processed correctly with Medicare. With the click of their *Blue Button*, you can easily download and save your health information and files to your computer, tablet, or mobile device, or print off an "On the Go" report to take with you to doctor appointments. A few other things the site conveniently keeps track of are your prescriptions, Part B deductible status, and a record of preventive services available to you.

**④ New ID cards**

Recent enrollment in a Medicare Advantage plan, Medicare Supplement, or Medicare Part D Prescription Drug Plan also means that you will have new cards arriving in the mail. Make sure you remember to take these along on your first visit to your primary care physician and any visit with a new doctor. Your doctor's office will want copies of the cards on file. This will ensure that there is no confusion when it comes to billing. You'll also want to make sure your pharmacy has the new ID cards on file.

**⑤ Prescription Medications**

At the beginning of the year, try to get your prescriptions filled early. Getting this taken care of early will ensure that you are made aware of any formulary changes in your plan. You should receive a notification of changes in your insurance company's drug list if it affects you, but in case you missed it, or it hasn't made it to your mailbox yet, you will at least be aware of the situation before it becomes a problem.

## ANNUAL RE-MARKETING

One last note about your annual Medicare housekeeping—if you currently have Option 1 or 2, your insurance company, agent, or agency will probably reach out to you multiple times a year to get you to consider a Medicare Advantage plan. Why? It's simple—they all make more money from Medicare Advantage plans. That's not to say you shouldn't consider it. Moving from a Medicare Supplement or a Medicare Part D Prescription Drug Plan into a Medicare Advantage plan may make a ton of sense for you. Just be aware that there may also be a financial motivation at play when you're approached.

# CHAPTER ELEVEN

# GROUP MEDICARE, EMPLOYER-BASED MEDICARE COVERAGE
## AND
# MEDICARE FOR VETERANS

Nearly one in five Medicare Advantage enrollees (19%) are in Group Medicare plans offered by employers and unions for their retirees. Under these arrangements, employers or unions contract with one or multiple insurance companies, and Medicare pays the insurer a fixed amount per enrollee to provide benefits covered by Medicare. The employer or union (and sometimes the retiree) may also pay a premium for additional benefits or lower cost-sharing. Companies like United Healthcare, Blue Cross and Blue Shield, Humana, and Aetna are the big companies in this space. The most common Group Medicare arrangements are Group Medicare Advantage plans, but other variations exist. Some offer commercial insurance look-alike plans and pair them with a Medicare Part D Group Medicare plan.

People on Group Medicare retirement accounts make up a disproportionately large share of Medicare Advantage enrollees in eight states: Michigan (49%), West Virginia (44%), New Jersey (40%), Wyoming

(36%), Illinois (35%), Maryland (35%), Kentucky (34%), and Delaware (31%) (Sources: PrepareforMedicare.com/sources).

## GROUP MEDICARE PLANS

These don't have to follow the same rules as the individual Medicare Advantage and Medicare Part D Prescription Drug Plans. Group Medicare plans are not available on the open market or Medicare.gov, nor can your independent Medicare insurance agent sell them, generally. These are plans designed by insurance companies at the specific request of a company to offer coverage for all of their retirees. If you're a retiree of this company, you're usually eligible to buy it for you and your partner or spouse. These Group Medicare plans can be fully customized—and often are. I've seen plans that eliminate member costs for hospitalizations, for instance. I've seen MOOPs as low as $1000 per year (almost unheard of in regular, individual Medicare Advantage), and I've seen prescription drug benefits with very low copays, no coverage gaps, and that cover non-Medicare approved medications like erectile dysfunction drugs.

It's a common misperception that if you have a Group Medicare plan offered to you through your company or your union, you have to take it. You do not. You can choose to opt out and go get other coverage. However, there are a lot of reasons you wouldn't want to do that.

1. If you're getting the plan for free or receiving a stipend or allowance from your former employer or union to pay for the plan partially or in full, dropping the plan will most likely end that stipend or allowance.

2. Once you drop your Group Medicare plan, many plans won't let you back on if you decide you made a mistake.

3. Since Group Medicare plans are normally highly customized, you won't be able to find a plan with such rich benefits on the open market as you have on a Group Medicare plan.

Can you drop or not participate in your Group Medicare plan? Sure. But be very careful. You've earned these benefits and probably paid for them out of your paycheck while working. If you drop them, **it's likely they won't let you back on the plan once you've made that choice.** That said, here's why you might consider dropping your Group Medicare plan:

1. The benefits offered are not as good as those found on the open market.

2. The company or union doesn't help you pay for monthly premiums.

3. The premiums are higher than what you can find on the open market.

4. The monthly premiums keep going up every year, and you think you can find a better deal elsewhere.

5. The benefits keep getting worse every year, and you think you can find a better deal elsewhere.

As I mentioned, every Group Medicare plan at every employer and union is likely different. If your company or union offers retiree medical coverage, it's wise to begin asking for the particulars from your HR Department or union representatives long before you decide to retire. You'll want to compare monthly premiums, drug and medical benefits, stipend or allowances received (or not) from your employer or union, MOOPs, lifetime dollar limits imposed . . . the list goes on. You can also do this if you've been on the Group Medicare plan for years. Essentially, you want to do a compare and contrast. Which one is *best* for you is going to depend on multiple factors too numerous to list here. Get the paperwork for your Group Medicare plan, and once you have this information, **it's wise to run these by the HR department *and* a good independent Medicare insurance agent to help you weigh the pros and cons.**

There are other employer-based options that don't fit neatly into the Group Medicare explanation above. These are called Employer Group Exchange arrangements.

# EMPLOYER-GROUP EXCHANGES

Employer Group Exchanges are companies who administer benefits for companies with retiree medical benefits, but instead of having them on a Group Medicare plan, they help transition them onto individual plans available on the open market. The two largest insurance agencies and consulting groups doing this nationwide are AON and Willis Towers Watson.

In the vast majority of these situations, the employer closes down their Group Medicare or retiree health plan, but because they're contractually obligated to provide retiree coverage, they use AON or Willis Towers Watson to help transition people to open-market individual plans. The companies often continue to pay their retirees a monthly or annual stipend or allowance through a Health Reimbursement Account (HRA). The company contracts with AON or Willis Towers Watson to help their retirees buy a plan and apply the stipend or allowance to their plan choices. This happens over the phone or via videoconference, sometimes spanning multiple calls between the retiree and an AON or Willis Towers Watson phone agent.

These phone reps take retirees through the first three choices outlined earlier in the book.

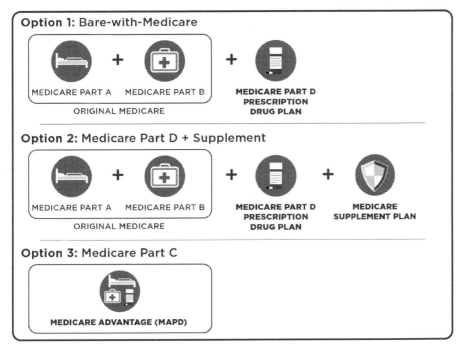

After they explain these options to the retiree, they may run them through additional product options such as add-on dental if the retiree wants Option #2, which of course, doesn't normally include dental coverage. Sometimes they might suggest that the retiree buy a hospital indemnity product that will pay lump sums should they be hospitalized or a cancer policy that does the same if someone gets cancer.

Often, these aren't necessary purchases. It all depends on the choices the retiree makes for their health and prescription drug coverage and how much they've got to spend with their employer's stipend or allowance. If the retiree has $120 a month to spend and they choose a $0 PPO Medicare Advantage plan, well, why not buy additional coverage?

Just like with Group Medicare, it's a common misperception that if you have benefits offered to you by your former employer or union through an Employer-Group Exchange, you have to take it. You do not. You can choose to opt out and get your own coverage on the open market. Again, there are a lot of reasons why you wouldn't want to do that.

If you get an allowance or stipend, it wouldn't make sense to ignore that. Most often, if you don't go through the employer-group exchange organization, you'll lose that allowance or stipend.

Can you not participate in the employer-group exchange process? Sure. But again, be very careful. It's true these exchanges offer the exact same plans available to you and everyone else on Medicare.gov or through insurance agents. However, **if you don't use an exchange, you'll likely lose your allowance or stipend.** You've earned those benefits and probably paid for them out of your paycheck while working. That said, here's why you might consider not participating in an employer-group exchange.

1. You do not get an allowance or stipend from your former employer.

2. You don't need or want the guidance the exchange telephone reps can provide and don't need help with plan selection.

# VETERANS

There are over nine million veterans over the age of sixty-five in the United States (Sources: PrepareforMedicare.com/sources).

Many of these veterans get their prescription drug benefits through the Veteran's Administration (VA) or TRICARE.

Throughout the book, I use the phrase "Medicare Advantage (MAPD)" and, as I've explained, what I'm referencing is the all-in-one combo Medicare Advantage product that includes Part D Prescription Drug benefits.

However, there are products specifically designed by Medicare insurance companies for veterans who get their prescriptions through the Veteran's Administration (VA) or TRICARE. These are known as Medicare Advantage "Only" products. The acronym or phrase for these plans is "MA-only." MA-only plans do not include the Part D prescription drug benefits.

More often than not, these plans come with all of the *extras* listed throughout the book that aren't included in Original Medicare, VA, or TRICARE benefits. These can include dollar amount allowances for dental, vision, hearing, access to wellness programs, OTC allowances, and more. Most, if not all, of these MA-only plans have a $0 monthly premium. They also have networks, just like all Medicare Advantage plans. I've included a few links around this topic on the website at PrepareforMedicare.com/links.

If you decide you want to explore this or other insurance options, my simple advice would be to find a good Medicare insurance agent. Unfortunately, not all Medicare insurance agents know the ins and outs of how Medicare works with VA and TRICARE. Normally, there's usually one in every town and only a handful in every city who really understand this, but they're hard to find as there's no special designation. **Your best bet for finding a Medicare insurance agent who knows this stuff through and through is for you to reach out to your veterans' network and ask for a referral. Odds are, there are one or two go-to agents in town most veterans use when they're on Medicare.**

**You might also call the Medicare insurance company and ask them. Aetna, Humana, and United Healthcare are all large Medicare insurance**

carriers who have dedicated teams within their companies who specifically develop and run these MA-only plans, specifically for Veterans.

# THE 2021 MEDICARE PART D SENIOR SAVINGS MODEL

In March of 2020, the Trump administration announced a new program for Medicare recipients to lower the cost of insulin. This is called the Part D Senior Savings Model and rolled out for a trial run for MAPD and Medicare Part D Prescription Drug Plans, effective 2021.

It was a voluntary participation program for Medicare insurance companies, and not all companies volunteered. However, those that did added this benefit to over 1,600 individual Medicare Advantage and Medicare Part D Prescription Drug Plans, making options available to Medicare consumers in all fifty states and Puerto Rico. The maximum insulin costs for people enrolled in one of those plans and who chose to participate is a maximum $35 copay for a month's supply for a broad range of insulins, including both pen and vial dosage forms for rapid-acting, short-acting, intermediate-acting, and long-acting insulins.

Insulin users who select a participating plan for 2021 are expected to save an average of $446 on out-of-pocket insulin costs over their 2020 insulin spending.

How do you find a plan that's participating in this program? It's as easy as heading over to Medicare.gov and filtering your search results on "Insulin Savings" to display participating plans. (See the DIY Chapter Nine for more on how to navigate Medicare.gov.)

# COVID-19 CHANGES

In March 2020, the World Health Organization declared the COVID-19 pandemic. Since then, life as we know it has dramatically changed. Healthcare and the way we consume it has and will continue to dramatically change as well. We've all been largely stuck in our homes, and many of us have put off planned surgeries or doctor's visits. As of this writing, things are beginning to open back up.

On March 13, 2020, President Trump made an emergency declaration under the Stafford Act and the National Emergencies Act, empowering The Centers for Medicare and Medicaid (CMS) to issue waivers to Medicare program requirements to support health care providers and patients during the pandemic. One of the first actions CMS took under that authority was to expand Medicare telehealth on March 17, 2020, allowing all beneficiaries to receive telehealth in any location, including their homes. Subsequently, CMS announced additional temporary rules and waivers to expand the scope of Medicare telehealth services, making it easier for more types of health care providers to offer a wider range of telehealth services to beneficiaries across the country. CMS observed immediate, dramatic increases in telehealth services (Sources: PrepareforMedicare.com/sources).

Thus, Medicare and Medicare insurance companies made a number of mid-year changes due to the 2020 COVID-19 pandemic. Some will be temporary changes, while others might be longer-lasting. It's too early to tell.

Medicare has an entire section of their website devoted to COVID-19. Highlights include:

- ✅ Medicare covers FDA-approved COVID-19 vaccines.

- ✅ Medicare covers the lab tests for COVID-19. You pay no out-of-pocket costs.

- ✅ Medicare covers FDA-authorized COVID-19 antibody (or "serology") tests if you were diagnosed with a known current, or known prior, COVID-19 infection or suspected of current or past COVID-19 infection.

- ✅ Medicare covers monoclonal antibody treatments for COVID-19.

- ✅ Medicare covers all medically necessary hospitalizations. This includes if you're diagnosed with COVID-19 and might otherwise have been discharged from the hospital after an inpatient stay, but, instead, you need to stay in the hospital under quarantine. You'll still pay for any hospital deductibles, copays, or coinsurances that apply.

Here's the link: https://www.Medicare.gov/medicare-coronavirus.

Many Medicare insurance companies have also waived COVID-19 testing and treatment and primary care office visit copays. Many also sent out care packages containing masks, hand sanitizer, and more to their membership and expanded access to healthcare providers via telehealth.

America's Health Insurance Plans (AHIP) is a national association representing insurance companies. They provide a nice summary of select member Health insurance companies' responses to COVID-19. You can click that link by going to the website PrepareforMedicare.com/links.

## THE TELEHEALTH EXPLOSION

Telehealth is loosely defined as the delivery of healthcare, health education, and health information services via remote technologies. Because many folks have been stuck in their homes and not getting routine in-person checkups or having planned procedures done inpatient or outpatient, Medicare and Medicare insurance companies have loosened their restrictions on telehealth. Since the beginning of the pandemic, some areas of the country saw *one hundred times* more telehealth claims in 2020 than in 2019 (Sources: PrepareforMedicare.com/sources).

Medicare and Medicare insurance companies have made temporary changes to the way they pay for telehealth. Among them:

- ✓ Medicare will pay physicians the same rate for telehealth services as they do for in-person visits for all diagnoses, not just those related to COVID-19, throughout the national public health emergency.

- ✓ Patients can be in their homes, or any other setting, to receive telehealth services.

- ✓ Patients do not need to have an existing relationship with the physician who is providing telehealth assistance.

- ✓ Physicians are allowed to waive or reduce cost-sharing for telehealth visits.

Physicians who are licensed in one state are allowed to see a patient in a different state.

As of this writing, we're still in the middle of the COVID-19 pandemic, but vaccine administration is on the rise. While many of these changes have been implemented, it remains to be seen whether or not they'll continue long-term. Vaccines are being distributed and have been administered to front-line personnel, and vaccinations are working their way through the population. The long-term administration and impacts are yet to be determined. I'll periodically update the website and will also cover this topic in my subscriber newsletters.

# CONCLUSION

At the beginning of the book, I promised to teach you what you need to know about Medicare, how to get it, how to understand what you're buying or bought, how it works, and whether it's the right plan for you.

I also told you that there are no *hacks* to Medicare. There are no shortcuts. It's not easy, but I shared what I could to make it easier.

Up until now, you've been overwhelmed with advertising, with what you thought were too many choices. Enrollment can be a pain and unclear. I promised to give you an insider's view on how to block out all the advertising and marketing noise and narrow your choices down without having to become a Medicare expert. I wrote the book to guide you toward making the right choices at the right time, in the right way for your individual needs, desires, and situation.

At this point, you should have a clear understanding of your options and how to engage them. Hopefully, I've demystified the process and provided a road map you can use. Be sure to grab the resources and find all of the links you need at PrepareforMedicare.com.

Lastly, as I've previously mentioned, I've worked for health insurance companies for most of my professional career. As a result, I freely acknowledge that I have a different perspective than others do on this subject. While I certainly can't speak for the entire health insurance industry, I can tell you that every person I've ever worked with for the last twenty-plus years is on your side.

That doesn't mean we're perfect, nor does it mean you have to like health insurance companies. But over the course of my career, I've never, ever met a single person inside an insurance company who sits around all day scheming up ways to limit your care so the company can squeeze out another dollar of profit. Not once. We all go to work every day trying to improve healthcare in our country, and we're proud of what we do.

I hope I've done what I've set out to do, and you're clear about how to move forward in the best way for you.

Congratulations on reading this book. I know it will help you. Now, please do gift a book to a friend who needs it as much as you did. I wish you wealth, wisdom and wellness!

# ACKNOWLEDGMENTS

When you've been doing something—anything—for more than twenty years, you tend to work with some great people. It might not seem like it from the outside, but the Medicare insurance industry is a small one on the inside. Many of us have known each other for years as we've moved from company to company, bumped into each other at conferences, and moved up the ranks. I can count any number of fantastic friends who work at competing or complementary companies, many of whom provided advice and encouragement for this book. Thank you especially to KvH, Billy P., Paul B., Eric W., K.S., Ray-Ray, Jay G., Lindsay R., Kirby A., Mark S., Mike G. and Mark O. There are of course, many others who chipped in and fact-checked for me but didn't want or think they somehow deserved an official acknowledgement. You know who you are. Thank you.

A special note of thanks goes to Honorée Corder, who helped bring this 10+ year idea to fruition. Her badassery is legendary and well-deserved. Also thank you to my editorial team, Alice Sullivan, Terry Stafford, Dino Marino and Jackie Dana, who helped me shape this book and make it awesome.

I'd also like to thank Matt De La Cruz at The Winning Minds Group. Matt's programs, goal-setting workshops, coaching, and approach to life quite literally supercharged my career almost before it began in the early 2000's. He's been an invaluable and inspirational professional friend ever since.

Finally, there's zero chance any of this exists without the love, support and guidance provided by my wife, Niki. I love you.

# APPENDIX

For an extended list of resources, be sure to visit
**www.PrepareforMedicare.com**

## HELPFUL OR INTERESTING WEBSITES THAT DON'T TRY TO SELL YOU ANYTHING:

**The Official US Government Site for Medicare**
https://www.Medicare.gov/

**The Official US Government Site for Social Security**
https://www.ssa.gov/benefits/medicare/

**Medicare Rights Center**
https://www.medicarerights.org or
https://www.medicareinteractive.org/

**Kaiser Family Foundation**
https://www.kff.org/medicare/

**State Health Assistance Programs National Network**
https://www.shiptacenter.org/

**Center for Medicare Advocacy**
https://medicareadvocacy.org/

**Senior Medicare Patrol**
https://www.smpresource.org/

**TRICARE For Life and Medicare**
https://tricare.mil/Plans/Eligibility/MedicareEligible

**National Coucil on Aging**
https://ncoa.org

# LARGE(ER) MEDICARE INSURANCE COMPANY WEBSITES
### (not a comprehensive list, and none specifically recommended or preferred by the author).

**Anthem Blue Cross and Blue Shield** – Blue Cross licensee for California; Blue Cross and Blue Shield of CO, CT, GA, IN, KY, MA, MO, NV, NH, NY, OH, VA, WI.

https://www.anthem.com/medicare/

**United Healthcare**

https://www.uhc.com/medicare

**Humana**

https://www.humana.com/medicare

**Aetna—A CVS Health Company**

https://www.aetnamedicare.com/

**Cigna**

https://www.cigna.com/medicare/

**Mutual of Omaha**

https://www.mutualofomaha.com/medicare-solutions

**WellCare—a Centene Company**

https://wellcare.com/medicare

**HCSC Blue Cross and Blue Shield of IL, TX, OK, NM, MT**

https://www.bcbsil.com/medicare

https://www.bcbstx.com/medicare

https://www.bcbsok.com/medicare

https://www.bcbsnm.com/medicare

https://www.bcbsmt.com/medicare

**Kaiser Permanente (CA, CO, GA, HI, MD, OR, VA, WA, DC)**

https://medicare.kaiserpermanente.org/wps/portal/medicare/plans/home

**Blue Cross and Blue Shield of Florida**

https://www.floridablue.com/medicare/

**SCAN Health Plan (CA)**
https://www.scanhealthplan.com/

**Tufts Health Plan (MA)**
https://www.tuftsmedicarepreferred.org/

# COMMON HYBRID AGENCY WEBSITES
### (not a comprehensive list, and none specifically recommended or preferred by the author)

**eHealth, Inc. (NASDAQ: EHTH)**
https://www.ehealthmedicare.com/

**GoHealth, Inc. (NASDAQ: GOCO)**
https://www.gohealth.com/medicare/

**SelectQuote, Inc. (NYSE: SLQT)**
https://medicare.selectquote.com/

**Assurance**
https://www.assurance.com/medicare

**HealthPlanOne**
https://medicareusa.com/

**Tranzact Insurance Solutions (owned by Willis Towers Watson; NASDAQ: WLTW)**
https://www.medicaresupplement.com/

https://www.medicareadvantage.com/

**HealthSpire (owned by CVS Health Corporation; NYSE: CVS)**
https://healthspire.com/

**HelloMedicare (owned by United Healthcare; NYSE: UNH)**
https://www.hellomedicare.com/

**HealthMarkets, Inc. (owned by United Healthcare; NYSE: UNH)**
https://www.healthmarkets.com/medicare/

# GLOSSARY

## MEDICARE ACRONYMS AND TERMS

**"Bare-with-Medicare"** – author's phrase used to refer to using Original Medicare Parts A and B *only* for medical insurance coverage "bare" of any Medicare Supplement to supplement coverage gaps.

**Medicare** – Federal health insurance for people over age sixty-five. Also available for certain people with disabilities who are under-age sixty-five and have ESRD or ALS.

**Medicare.gov** – Medicare's consumer-facing website.

**Medicare Part A** – hospital insurance; covers inpatient hospital care, skilled nursing facility, hospice, surgery, home health care.

**Medicare Part B** – helps pay for services from doctors and other health care providers, lab tests, outpatient care, home health care, and durable medical equipment.

**Medicare Part C** – also known as Medicare Advantage. These are "combo" products of Medicare Parts A, B and D. There is no "public" option Medicare Part C offering; all are sold by authorized Medicare insurance companies. Commonly referred by the acronym, **MAPD**, which stands for **M**edicare **A**dvantage **P**rescription **D**rug. Less commonly used or known, but can also refer to MA-only plans, DSNP plans or SNP plans.

**Medicare Part D** – Also referred to as a **PDP**, a Part D Plan or a Medicare Part D **P**rescription **D**rug **P**lan. These are stand-alone Prescription Drug Plans and do not cover any medical procedures—they only cover prescription drugs. Medicare Part D is also the **P**rescription **D**rug 'PD' in an MA**PD** plan. There are no "public option" Medicare Part D Prescription Drug Plans and these are only sold by authorized Medicare insurance companies.

**Original Medicare** – refers to Medicare Parts A and B only.

**Medicare Supplement** – also known as **Medigap** – There are no "public option" Medicare Supplement plans—only sold by authorized Medicare insurance companies. These policies help fill "gaps" in Original Medicare. Plans are standardized by letters. Most popular and comprehensive plans are Plan F and Plan C (if eligible for Medicare prior to 1/1/2020) or Plan G and Plan N.

## COMMON MEDICARE ADVANTAGE ACRONYMS AND TERMS

**Medicare Advantage plans** use networks of doctors and hospitals. There are three common versions of these:

**1** **HMO** – "**H**ealth **M**aintenance **O**rganization." You generally cannot use any doctors out of the Medicare insurance company plan's network, although there are occasional exceptions.

**2** **HMO-POS** – "**H**ealth **M**aintenance **O**rganization—**P**oint **of** **S**ervice." While rare, these plans let you go out of the plan's network, often requiring a referral from a doctor who is in the network. Your costs are typically higher if you go outside of the Medicare insurance company's network.

**3** **PPO** – "**P**referred **P**rovider **O**rganization." You can use any doctors and hospitals in and out of the plan's network. Your costs are typically higher if you go outside of the Medicare insurance company's network. Out of network providers do not have to accept you as a patient nor is there a contractual obligation for them to bill your Medicare insurance company.

**MA-Only** – **M**edicare **A**dvantage **Only** Plans are Medicare Part C plans *without* prescription drug benefits embedded. Most often used only for Medicare recipients who have TRICARE and/or get their prescriptions through the Veteran's Administration.

**DSNP** – **D**ual-**S**pecial **N**eeds **P**lans are only for people who qualify for both Medicare and Medicaid.

**SNP** – **S**pecial **N**eeds **P**lans refer to Medicare Advantage plans for people with special, specific healthcare needs.

## COMMON MEDICARE ENROLLMENT AND ELECTION PERIODS
**(when you can sign up for or change coverage):**

**AEP** – the **A**nnual **E**lection **P**eriod. Runs from October 15 - December 7 every year. During this period, anyone with Medicare can change their Medicare Advantage plans or Medicare Part D Prescription Drug Plans for the following year. The AEP does not apply to Medicare Supplement plans.

**ICEP** – **I**nitial **C**overage **E**lection **P**eriod. This only matters if you defer signing up for Medicare Part B for some reason, such as working past age sixty-five and maintaining employer-based health insurance coverage during that time. The ICEP is your first opportunity to choose a Medicare Advantage plan instead of Original Medicare. When you join Medicare Part B later, your ICEP is the three months before your Part B coverage takes effect. If you enroll in Part B when you turn sixty-five, your ICEP is the same as your IEP.

**IEP** – the **I**nitial **E**nrollment **P**eriod. When you're first eligible for Medicare, you have a seven-month Initial Enrollment Period to sign up for Part A and/or Part B. If you're eligible for Medicare when you turn sixty-five, you can sign up during the three months before the month you turn sixty-five, the month you turn sixty-five, and the three months after you turn sixty-five.

**Medicare Supplement Open Enrollment Period** – automatically starts the month you're sixty-five and enrolled in Medicare Part B. If you defer Medicare Part B because, for example, you're working and have employer-sponsored healthcare coverage, the period starts when you finally do elect Medicare Part B. This is a one-time, six-month enrollment window. After this period, you may not be able to buy a Medicare Supplement policy without answering health questions. If you're able to buy one, it may cost more due to past or present health problems.

**OEP** – the **O**pen **E**nrollment **P**eriod. Runs from January 1 - March 31 each year. If you're enrolled in a Medicare Advantage plan, you can switch to a different Medicare Advantage plan or switch back to Original Medicare and buy a Medicare Part D Prescription Drug Plan once during this time. Also known as the **M**edicare **A**dvantage **O**pen **E**nrollment **P**eriod (MAOEP)

**SEP** – **S**pecial **E**nrollment **P**eriod(s). These are special, one-off events in life that trigger new enrollment or change windows outside of the AEP and OEP.

## OTHER COMMON MEDICARE INSURANCE TERMS:

**ANOC** – **A**nnual **N**otification **o**f **C**hange. Notice you receive from your Medicare Advantage or Medicare Part D plan in late September. It includes any changes in coverage, costs, or service area that will be effective on January 1 of the upcoming year.

**Coinsurance** – the share (percentage) of the claim the insurance company will pay; the remaining is yours to pay.

**Copay** – a flat fee paid when you receive specific health care services, such as a doctor visit, prescription drugs or inpatient hospitalization.

**Deductible** – a defined amount of money you must pay before an insurance company will pay a claim.

**Medicaid** – a state government program that helps pay health care costs for people with limited income and resources. In order to qualify for a DSNP, you must have Medicare and Medicaid.

**Medicare Excess Charges** – doctors who do not accept Medicare "assignment" may charge up to 15% more than the Medicare Part B rate for a particular service. Rare, but when they occur, the additional costs are passed on and billed directly to you.

**MOOP** – acronym for **M**aximum **O**ut **O**f **P**ocket found on all Medicare Advantage plans. Limits the amount of annual medical spending financial exposure.

**SNF** – **S**killed **N**ursing **F**acilities. Post-hospital care: can include services such as administration of medications, tube feedings, and wound care. SNFs can be part of nursing homes or hospitals. This is not long-term care, nor does Medicare cover traditional long-term care (custodial care).

# WHO IS MATT FERET?

Matt Feret began his professional career mowing lawns at age ten. He's surprised to have emerged many years later to find himself a Medicare insurance industry veteran, which *still* sounds weird in his head when he types it. He's made professional stops at Anthem, Humana, HCSC, CVS Health/Aetna and some he'd rather forget. The thoughts and opinions expressed in this publication are those of the author only, and are not the thoughts and opinions of any current or former employer of the author. Nor is this publication made by, on behalf of, or endorsed or approved by any current or former employer of the author.

He is passionate about making it easy for people pick the right Medicare plan *for them* without the perceived requisite pain and suffering. Matt really likes talking about Medicare, personal finance, and retirement issues and feels happy when helping people understand them. He believes it's part of his purpose for being on the planet. The pursuit of laugher and happiness is one of his favorite pastimes.

Matt follows the Virginia Tech Hokies, likes attending obnoxiously loud heavy metal concerts, baseball games that go into extra innings and hiking. He'd bet you his 8th grade English teacher is floored he actually wrote a book. He also really loves his wife and kids who tolerate living with him in a suburb of Chicago. The family also includes two cats named Puck and Blossom which apparently are named after Shakespeare characters. His kids made him add their names to his bio.

Matt loves public and private speaking—come connect with him on the interwebs!

Company Name: MF Media, LLC

Email: mf@mattferet.com

Website: mattferet.com

LinkedIn: linkedin.com/in/mattferet

Twitter: @feret_matt

Facebook: https://www.facebook.com/mattferet/

# INDEX

## A

## B

# C

# D

# E

# N

# O

# P

# R

# S

# T

# U

# V

Made in the USA
Middletown, DE
18 January 2022

58927457R00155